HEINEMANN MODULAR MATHEMATICS *for* LONDON AS AND A-LEVEL

Statistics 4

Greg Attwood   Gill Dyer   Gordon Skipworth

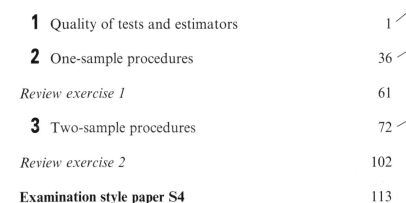

Heinemann

Edexcel
Success through qualifications

Heinemann Educational Publishers,
a division of Heinemann Publishers (Oxford) Ltd,
Halley Court, Jordan Hill, Oxford, OX2 8EJ

OXFORD   JOHANNESBURG   BLANTYRE   MELBOURNE
AUCKLAND   GABORONE   PORTSMOUTH NH (USA)   CHICAGO

First published 2001

05   04   03   02   01

10   9   8   7   6   5   4   3   2   1

ISBN 0 435 51085 1

Cover design by Gecko Limited

Original design by Geoffrey Wadsley; additional design work by Jim Turner

Typeset and illustrated by Tech-Set Limited, Gateshead, Tyne and Wear

Printed in Great Britain by Scotprint

Acknowledgements:

The publisher's and authors' thanks are due to Edexcel for permission to
reproduce questions from past examination papers. These are marked with an [E].
   The answers have been provided by the authors and are not the responsibility
of the examining board.

About this book

This book is designed to provide you with the best preparation possible for your Edexcel S4 exam. The series authors are senior examiners and moderators themselves and have a good understanding of Edexcel's requirements.

Use this **new edition** to prepare for the new 6-unit specification. Use the first edition (*Heinemann Modular Mathematics for London AS and A-Level*) if you are preparing for the 4-module syllabus.

Finding your way around

To help to find your way around when you are studying and revising use the:

- **edge marks** (shown on the front page) – these help you to get to the right chapter quickly;
- **contents list** – this lists the headings that identify key syllabus ideas covered in the book so you can turn straight to them;
- **index** – if you need to find a topic the **bold** number shows where to find the main entry on a topic.

Remembering key ideas

We have provided clear explanations of the key ideas and techniques you need throughout the book. Key ideas you need to remember are listed in a **summary of key points** at the end of each chapter and marked like this in the chapters:

■ **A type I error occurs if H_0 is rejected when it is in fact true.**

Exercises and exam questions

In this book questions are carefully graded so they increase in difficulty and gradually bring you up to exam standard.

- **past exam questions** are marked with an [E];
- **review exercises** on pages 61 and 102 help you practise answering questions from several areas of mathematics at once, as in the real exam;
- **exam-style practice paper** – this is designed to help you prepare for the exam itself;
- **answers** are included at the end of the book – use them to check your work.

Contents

3 Two-sample procedures

Quality of tests and estimators

1

In the practical world many of the applications of statistics are concerned with the process of taking samples and using them to make inferences about the means and variances of the populations from which they were taken. This book is mainly concerned with a number of hypothesis tests that enable you to use samples to make such inferences. Chapter 2 is concerned with confidence intervals and hypothesis tests that can be made using a single sample, and the related confidence intervals. Chapter 3 is concerned with confidence intervals and hypothesis tests when two independent samples are taken.

As in Statistics 3 we will use italicised capital letters such as X, Y, R, etc. to represent random variables, and small italicised letters such as x, y, r, etc. to represent particular values of the random variables X, Y, R, etc. Population parameters will usually be represented by Greek letters such as μ for the mean and σ^2 for the variance, while Roman letters such as $\bar{x}$ and s^2 will represent sample values. In the case of the binomial distribution we shall continue to use p to describe the population proportion as in Statistics 2.

We begin in this chapter by looking at hypothesis testing in greater detail, considering the possible errors that can occur when you are hypothesis testing, and the effectiveness of statistical tests. Later you will consider methods of assessing the quality of estimators.

1.1 Hypothesis testing

It has been said that hypothesis tests exist in order to give the facts a chance to disprove the null hypothesis. Let us look in more detail at what you do in such a test.

If the observed value of the variable is not part of the critical region (the set of values that have a small probability of occurring under the null hypothesis) then you do not have sufficient evidence to reject the null hypothesis. You do not look mathematically at the alternative hypothesis; it is only if the observed value falls in the critical region (i.e. if the probability of getting the observed value under the null hypothesis is very small, typically $\leqslant 0.05$) that you accept the alternative hypothesis. The decision about the null hypothesis is made by using the null hypothesis, and the only part played by the alternative hypothesis is to decide whether the test is to be one- or two-tailed.

In Statistics 3 (page 45) you considered the weights of students when they joined a college, and were interested in whether or not the mean weight of the new entry was higher than the usual mean weight. The distribution of the weights of all students at the college when they enrolled was normal, with a mean of 70 kg and a standard deviation of 7.5 kg. A random sample of 90 students from the new entry had a mean weight of 71.6 kg and it was assumed that the standard deviation had not changed.

The null and alternative hypotheses were

$$H_0 : \mu = 70 \text{ and } H_1 : \mu > 70,$$

and the significance level was 5%.

The critical region for Z was found from the tables to be $Z \geqslant 1.6449$. For the sample with $n = 90$ and $\bar{x} = 71.6$ the value of the test statistic $Z = \dfrac{\overline{X} - \mu}{\frac{\sigma}{\sqrt{n}}}$ was

$$z = \frac{71.6 - 70}{\dfrac{7.5}{\sqrt{90}}} = 2.0239$$

This was in the critical region and H_0 was rejected.

This is shown on the diagram below:

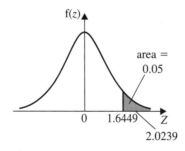

The diagram shows that 2.0239 is in the critical region.

In practical terms it is often more helpful to know the critical region for the test statistic $\overline{X}$.

If $Z \geqslant 1.6449$ then the smallest value of $\overline{X}$ in the critical region can be calculated as follows:

$$Z \geqslant 1.6449$$

so

$$\frac{\overline{X} - \mu}{\frac{\sigma}{\sqrt{n}}} \geqslant 1.6449$$

$$\overline{X} \geqslant 1.6449 \times \frac{7.5}{\sqrt{90}} + 70$$

i.e.

$$\overline{X} \geqslant 71.3 \ldots$$

so a value of $\bar{x} \geqslant 71.3$ would lead you to reject H_0, and any value of $\bar{x}$ such that $\bar{x} < 71.3$ would not provide enough evidence to reject H_0. The diagram below illustrates this:

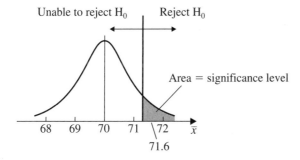

If, as above, $\bar{x} = 71.6$ it will fall into the critical region as shown, and H_0 will be rejected.

1.2 Type I errors

Notice that above it was said that the alternative hypothesis is accepted only if the probability of getting the observed value under the null hypothesis is small. In the example above, even if H_0 were true the value $71.6\,\text{kg}$ observed for $\bar{x}$ could still occur. If you took a large number of samples, then theoretically you would get a value for $\bar{x} \geqslant 71.3$ in 5% of them, and in these cases you would be rejecting the null hypothesis when it was in fact true.

Rejecting the null hypothesis when it is true is called a **type I error**, and the probability of it happening is called the **probability of a type I error** and is usually denoted by the Greek letter α.

■ **A type I error occurs if H_0 is rejected when it is in fact true. The probability of a type I error is the probability of obtaining a value of the test statistic that lies in the critical region assuming that H_0 is true.**

1.3 Type II errors

There is of course the possibility that the true mean of the new intake of students is greater than 70 kg and that you were correct in rejecting the null hypothesis when $\bar{x}$ was 71.6 kg. Although we do not know the true value of the mean weight of the new students, let us suppose that it is in fact 71 kg, and that the standard deviation stays the same as before. You could still get a range of different values for the sample mean $\bar{x}$. The diagram below shows the probability distribution assuming a true mean of 71 kg and how it relates to the critical value 71.3 kg.

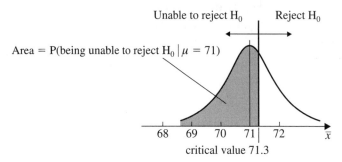

As you can see from the diagram, you could well have obtained a value of 71.6 kg for $\bar{x}$, in which case you would have been right in rejecting H_0. However, you could, for example, have got a value of 71 kg for $\bar{x}$. In this case you would not have had sufficient evidence to reject H_0 since $71 < 71.3$ (the critical value), even though H_0 was wrong (remember $H_0 : \mu = 70$). An error in which there is insufficient evidence to reject H_0 when it is wrong is called a **type II error**. The probability of making a type II error is usually denoted by the Greek letter β. Of course, if you do not know the exact value of the mean of the new intake of students, you cannot calculate the **probability of a type II error** (and if you did know it there would be no need to conduct the test), but if it was 71 kg as supposed above then you could calculate it as follows:

$$P(\text{type II error}) = P(\bar{X} < 71.3 \mid \mu = 71)$$

$$= P\left(Z < \frac{71.3 - 71}{\frac{7.5}{\sqrt{90}}} \right)$$

$$= P(Z < 0.379\dots)$$

$$= 0.65 \text{ (2 d.p.)}$$

■ **A type II error occurs if there is insufficient evidence to reject H_0 when it is false. The probability of a type II error is the probability of obtaining a value of the test statistic that does not lie in the critical region assuming H_1 is true.**

To summarise:

You have two possible outcomes to a significance test – either you have insufficient evidence to reject H_0 or it is rejected.

You have two possible real situations – H_0 is true or H_0 is false.

If you do not have sufficient evidence to reject H_0 when it is true then there is no error.

If you reject H_0 when it is untrue then again there is no error.

If you reject H_0 when it is true you commit a type I error.

If you do not reject H_0 when it is untrue then you commit a type II error.

These can be put in the form of a table as shown below:

	H_0 **true**	H_0 **false**
H_0 rejected	Type I error	No error
Insufficient evidence to reject H_0	No error	Type II error

Relation between type I and type II errors

In the example involving the mean weights of students you looked at the possibilities of both type I and type II errors, but you did not consider how the two were interrelated.

By superimposing the two figures you will be able to see what the effect of changing the significance level has on each of the two types of error.

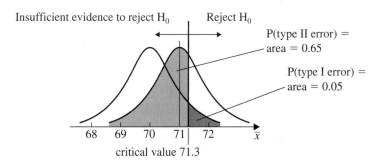

In the case illustrated above, the probability of committing a type II error is quite high and you may feel that it is a good idea to reduce the probability of a type II error. By looking at the diagram you will see that if you increase the significance level (i.e. move the critical value to the left in this case), this would decrease the probability of a type II error, but increase the probability of a type I error. On the other hand, if you decrease the significance level, the probability of a type I error decreases and the probability of a type II error increases. If you make α too small, you will end up being too conservative and always not having enough evidence to reject the null hypothesis (i.e. that there is no change in the mean weight of the new intake), while if you make α too high you will end up following false trails and thinking that a significant change has taken place when it hasn't. Experience has shown that in most cases a value of 5% for α is acceptable.

This does not mean that other significance levels are never used. When, for example, the results of the research are highly important and money is no object, it may be worth following up remoter possibilities. In such cases a 1% significance level might be used. If, however, the results are not as important and money is very tight, a significance level of 10% might be used. An alternative method of reducing the probability of a type II error is to increase the sample size, but you will appreciate that more cost is linked to increased sample size.

Although in the above case the alternative hypothesis was that $\mu > 70$, the same ideas may be applied when the alternative hypothesis is that the parameter is $<$ or $\neq$ a given value. The diagrams for all three cases follow. Notice that this time the diagrams are placed one above the other instead of being superimposed. This adds clarity when you are calculating the two errors rather than considering the effect of changing the critical value. It is always a good idea to sketch out what you want to find, so that you can see what it is you will have to calculate.

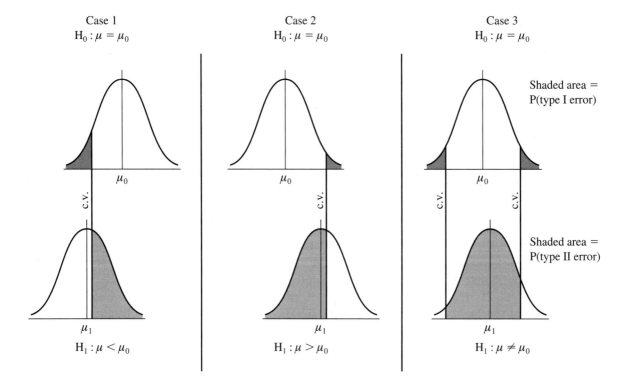

Case 1
$H_0 : \mu = \mu_0$

Case 2
$H_0 : \mu = \mu_0$

Case 3
$H_0 : \mu = \mu_0$

Shaded area = P(type I error)

Shaded area = P(type II error)

μ_0

c.v.

μ_1

$H_1 : \mu < \mu_0$

$H_1 : \mu > \mu_0$

$H_1 : \mu \neq \mu_0$

Notice in the three cases the relationship of the shaded areas representing the probability of type I and type II errors and how they fall either side of the critical value or, in case 3, either side of the two critical values.

Example 1

The weight of jam in a jar, measured in grams, is distributed normally with a mean of 150 and a standard deviation of 5. The production process occasionally leads to a change in the mean weight of jam per jar but the standard deviation remains unaltered.

The manager monitors the production process. For every new batch she takes a random sample of 25 jars and weighs their contents to see if there has been any reduction in the mean weight of jam per jar.

Find the critical values for the test statistic $\overline{X}$, the mean weight of jam in a sample of 25 jars, using

(a) a 5% level of significance,
(b) a 1% level of significance.

Given that the true value of μ for the new batch is in fact 147,

(c) Find the probability of a type II error for each of the above critical regions.

The appropriate test is a hypothesis test for the mean of a normal distribution (this was dealt with in Statistics 3, section 3.7).

(a) $H_0 : \mu = 150$ $H_1 : \mu < 150$ (i.e. a one-tailed test); $n = 25$ and $\sigma = 5$
The 5% critical region for Z is $Z \leqslant -1.6449$ so reject H_0 if

$$\frac{\overline{X} - 150}{\frac{5}{\sqrt{25}}} \leqslant -1.6449$$

That is, the critical region for $\overline{X}$ is

$$\overline{X} \leqslant \frac{5}{\sqrt{25}} \times (-1.6449) + 150$$

so $\quad\quad \overline{X} \leqslant 148.3551$

(b) The 1% critical region for Z is $Z \leqslant -2.3263$ so reject H_0 if

$$\frac{\overline{X} - 150}{\frac{5}{\sqrt{25}}} \leqslant -2.3263$$

That is, the critical region for $\overline{X}$ is

$$\overline{X} \leqslant \frac{5}{\sqrt{25}} \times (-2.3263) + 150$$

so $\quad\quad \overline{X} \leqslant 147.6737$

(c) 5% test: P(type II error) $= P(\bar{X} > 148.3551 \mid \mu = 147)$

$$= P\left(Z > \frac{148.3551 - 147}{\frac{5}{\sqrt{25}}} \right)$$

$$= P(Z > 1.3551) \text{ [use 1.36]}$$

$$= 1 - 0.9131$$

$$= 0.0869$$

Note calculator gives 0.08769

1% test: P(type II error) $= P(\bar{X} > 147.6737 \mid \mu = 147)$

$$= P\left(Z > \frac{147.6737 - 147}{\frac{5}{\sqrt{25}}} \right)$$

$$= P(Z > 0.6737) \text{ [use 0.67]}$$

$$= 1 - 0.7486$$

$$= 0.2514$$

Note calculator gives 0.25025

The sets of values for the two significance levels are illustrated below.

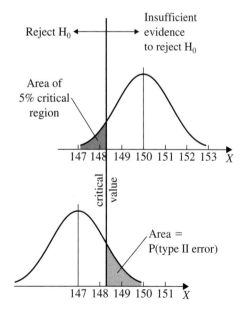

5% significance level

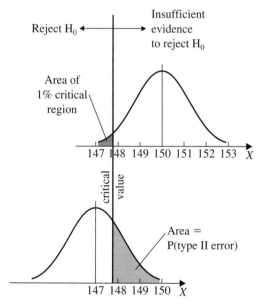

1% significance level

Notice how in this example if we try to *reduce* P(type I error) then P(type II error) *increases*. This can be seen on the two diagrams and illustrates the point made earlier. A more detailed study of the interplay between these two probabilities follows later in this chapter. However, you should be aware of this feature, and appreciate one of the reasons why we do not always use a significance level that is very small. The value of 5% has already been mentioned as a commonly used level, and in a situation where a particular significance level is not given this value is recommended.

Example 2

Bags of sugar having a nominal weight of 1 kg are filled by a machine. From past experience it is known that the weight, X kg, of sugar in the bags is normally distributed with a standard deviation of 0.04 kg. At the beginning of each week a random sample of 10 bags is taken in order to see if the machine needs to be reset. A test is then carried out at the 5% significance level with $H_0 : \mu = 1.00$ kg and $H_1 : \mu \neq 1.00$ kg.

(a) Find the critical region for this test.
(b) Given that the sample taken has a mean of 1.02 kg, test whether or not the mean has changed.
(c) Assuming that the mean weight has in fact changed to 1.02 kg, find the type I and type II errors for this test.

(a) Since this is a two-tailed test you allow 2.5% in each tail.

The distribution of $\bar{X}$ is modelled by $N\left(1.0, \dfrac{0.04^2}{10}\right)$.

From the tables the critical region for Z is $Z > 1.96$ or $Z < -1.96$.

The critical values for $\bar{X}$ are given by $\bar{x} = 1 \pm 1.96 \times \sqrt{\dfrac{0.04^2}{10}}$

$$= 0.9752 \text{ and } 1.0248$$

The critical region is $\bar{X} \leqslant 0.9752$ and $\bar{X} \geqslant 1.0248$.

(b) No. Since 1.02 is not in the critical region there is insufficient evidence that the mean has changed.

(c) The type I error for this test will be the same as the significance level $= 0.05$, so only the type II error needs to be found.

Below is a sketch showing the area to be found.

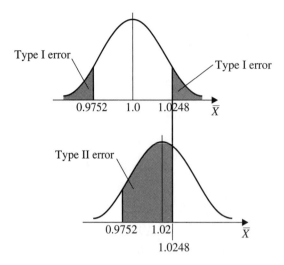

The area required lies between $\overline{X} = 0.9752$ and $\overline{X} = 1.0248$ given that $\overline{X}$ is now modelled by $N\left(1.02, \dfrac{0.04^2}{10}\right)$.

The probability of a type II error is given by

$$P(0.9752 < \overline{X} < 1.0248) = \Phi\left(\frac{1.0248 - 1.02}{\dfrac{0.04}{\sqrt{10}}}\right) - \Phi\left(\frac{0.9752 - 1.02}{\dfrac{0.04}{\sqrt{10}}}\right)$$

$$= \Phi(0.38) - \Phi(-3.54)$$

$$= 0.6480 - (1 - 0.9998)$$

$$= 0.6478$$

| Calculator gives 0.6476 |

Calculating type I and type II errors for discrete distributions

As with continuous data, there are three possible alternative hypotheses for discrete data. When illustrating discrete data a bar chart has to be used. The lengths of the bars represent the probabilities of the different values of the variable. These lengths change as the parameter changes. The three cases are illustrated in the following diagram for a binomial distribution with $n = 10$, and with the null hypothesis $H_0 : p = 0.5$.

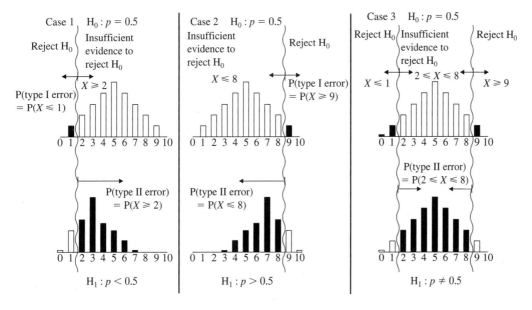

The actual values of p used in the lower diagrams are $p = 0.3$ for $H_1 : p < 0.5$, $p = 0.7$ for $H_1: p > 0.5$ and $p = 0.45$ for $H_1: p \neq 0.5$.

Note that in previous hypothesis tests based on parameters the population parameters, represented by Greek letters, have been used. For example, in example 1 $H_0 : \mu = 150$ and $H_1 : \mu < 150$ were used. In this section it would have been appropriate to use π when specifying the hypotheses. For example, $H_0 : \pi = 0.5$, $H_1 : \pi \neq 0.5$. However, to be consistent with section 4.8 in Statistics 2 we will use p to represent both the population and the sample value.

Example 3

The treatment for a certain illness has a probability of success of 0.45. A new treatment is being researched and, in a trial of 20 people, 13 were successfully treated using the new drug.

(a) Conduct an appropriate hypothesis test to examine whether or not there is enough evidence at the 5% significance level to suggest that the new drug is an improvement over the old one. Choose your critical region so that the probability of an observation lying in the critical region is $\leqslant 0.05$.
(b) Calculate the probability of a type I error.

Further research on the new drug showed that the true probability of a successful cure was 0.5.
(c) Use the information given above to calculate the probability of a type II error having been made in part (a).

(a) The appropriate test here is one for the proportion p of a binomial distribution (dealt with in Statistics 2). The appropriate hypotheses are

$$H_0 : p = 0.45 \quad H_1 : p > 0.45$$

Let X represent the number of people successfully treated using the new drug.

$$\therefore \qquad X \sim B(20, 0.45).$$

Note: sometimes a question may require you to use a critical region as close as possible to 0.05 – see Statistics 2, page 102.

You need to find a value c such that

$$P(X \geqslant c) \leqslant 0.05 \text{ (you are using a 5\% significance level)}$$

Now the binomial is a discrete distribution which can be divided into two parts: those values $\geqslant c$ and those $< c$, i.e. those $\leqslant c - 1$. This is shown on the right.

These two halves add up to 1. Thus $P(X \geqslant c) \leqslant 0.05$ is the same as

$$1 - P(X \leqslant c - 1) \leqslant 0.05$$
or
$$1 - 0.05 \leqslant P(X \leqslant c - 1)$$
$$0.95 \leqslant P(X \leqslant c - 1)$$

Using the table for the cumulative binomial distribution function (Appendix, Table 1) with $n = 20$, $p = 0.45$ you get

$$P(X \leqslant 12) = 0.9420 \text{ so } P(X \geqslant 13) = 1 - 0.9420 = 0.0580$$
$$P(X \leqslant 13) = 0.9786 \text{ so } P(X \geqslant 14) = 1 - 0.9786 = 0.0214$$

In this case $\qquad\qquad c - 1 = 13 \text{ or } c = 14$

Therefore you would need $X \geqslant 14$ in order to obtain sufficient evidence against H_0.
$X = 13$ so there is insufficient evidence to reject H_0 at the 5% level of significance.

(b) $\qquad\qquad P(\text{type I error}) = P(X \geqslant 14)$
$$= 1 - P(X \leqslant 13)$$
$$= 1 - 0.9786$$
$$= 0.0214$$

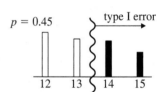

This is much less than 0.05 and, as explained earlier, it happens because the binomial distribution is discrete and only integer values of X are possible.

(c) $\qquad\qquad P(\text{type II error}) = P(X < 14 \mid p = 0.5)$
$$= P(X \leqslant 13 \mid p = 0.5)$$
$$= 0.9423$$

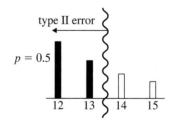

This question shows that again a high probability of a type II error exists when you have a low probability of a type I error. In a case such as this, you have the choice between setting the type I error to a low value and rejecting possible advances in medical treatments, or setting it to a high value and accepting the alternative hypothesis too readily, with the consequences of wasting time and money on a treatment that brings no benefits. Although the significance level chosen in this case was 5%, the probability of a type I error in this case is much smaller than 5%. There are other alternative courses of action that you can choose in such cases. One is to carry out the experiment a number of times (a process known as replication), then if you get the same result each time you can put much more reliance on the result. Alternatively you can conduct the test again with a larger number of people taking part. This would enable you to get the probability of a type I error which was nearer to the selected significance level. In the analysis of medical data the significance level is sometimes much smaller than 5%.

Example 4

Accidents occur on a stretch of motorway at a rate of 6 per month. Many of the accidents that occur involve vehicles skidding into the back of other vehicles. By way of a trial, a new type of road surface, said to reduce the risk of vehicles skidding, is laid on this stretch of road. During the first month of operation 4 accidents occur.

(a) Test whether or not there is evidence that there has been an improvement. Use a 5% level of significance.
(b) Calculate the type I error for this test.
(c) If the true rate of accidents occurring with this type of road surface was 3.5, calculate the probability of a type II error.

The appropriate test is a hypothesis test for the mean of a Poisson distribution (dealt with in Statistics 2).

(a) You are dealing with a Poisson distribution, so let $\lambda =$ the rate of accidents in a month, and X the number of accidents in any given month; then the hypotheses are

$H_0 : \lambda = 6$ (i.e. no change) $H_1 : \lambda < 6$ (i.e. fewer accidents)

From Appendix, Table 2, $P(X \leqslant 4 \mid \lambda = 6) = 0.2851$.
This is more than 5%, so you do not have enough evidence to reject H_0. The rate of accidents per month has not changed.

(b) In order to reject H_0 you required a value c such that

$$P(X \leqslant c \mid \lambda = 6) < 0.05$$

> Note you could have specified as close as possible to 5% (see Statistics 2 pages 99–102).

From Appendix, Table 2, with $\lambda = 6$:

$$P(X \leqslant 2) = 0.0620$$

and
$$P(X \leqslant 1) = 0.0174$$

So the critical value c is 1, and the critical region for this test is $X \leqslant 1$.

A type I error occurs when you reject H_0 when it is true, and the probability of this happening is $P(X \leqslant 1) = 0.0174$. This is again smaller than the 5% you were aiming for.

(c) A type II error occurs when you do not have sufficient evidence to reject H_0 when H_1 is true. If $\lambda = 3.5$ then H_0 is not true. You do not have sufficient evidence to reject H_0 if $X \geqslant 2$ so

$$P(\text{type II error} \mid \lambda = 3.5) = P(X \geqslant 2 \mid \lambda = 3.5)$$
$$= 1 - P(X \leqslant 1 \mid \lambda = 3.5)$$
$$= 1 - 0.1359$$
$$= 0.8641$$

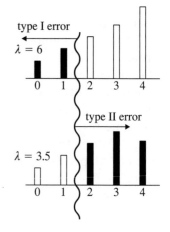

Notice that in the above example you used the opposite tail of the distribution to that used in example 3. This happens because the alternative hypothesis is $H_1 : \lambda < 6$. There is another form of the alternative hypothesis that occurs: this is when you ask whether there has been a change either up or down. In such cases a two-tailed test is used. This process is shown in the next example.

Example 5

A coin is tossed 20 times and a head is obtained on 7 occasions.

(a) Test to see whether or not the coin is biased.
(b) Calculate the type I error for this test.
(c) Given that the coin is biased and that this bias causes the head to appear 3 times for each tail that appears, calculate the type II error for the test.

(a) This is a test for the proportion of a binomial distribution, and since you are testing to see if the coin is biased in either direction, a two-tailed test has to be used. The hypotheses are

$$H_0 : p = 0.5 \quad H_1 : p \neq 0.5$$

Let X represent the number of heads obtained.

Assuming H_0 is true then $X \sim B(20, 0.5)$.

For a two-tailed test at the 5% significance level you require values c_1 and c_2 such that

$$P(X \leqslant c_1) \leqslant 0.025 \text{ and } P(X \geqslant c_2) \leqslant 0.025$$
$$(\text{or } P(X \leqslant c_2 - 1) \geqslant 0.975)$$

From Appendix, Table 1: $\qquad P(X \leqslant 6) = 0.0577$

and $\qquad\qquad\qquad\qquad P(X \leqslant 5) = 0.0207$

so the value of $c_1 = 5$.

Also, $\quad P(X \geqslant 14) = 1 - P(X \leqslant 13) = 1 - 0.9423 = 0.0577$
$\qquad P(X \geqslant 15) = 1 - P(X \leqslant 14) = 1 - 0.9793 = 0.0207$

so the value of $c_2 = 15$.

(Alternatively $P(X \leqslant 13) = 0.9423$ and $P(X \leqslant 14) = 0.9793$ so $c_2 - 1 = 14$ and $c_2 = 15$).

Thus the critical region for X is $X \leqslant 5$ or $X \geqslant 15$. As 7 falls between 5 and 15 there is insufficient evidence to reject H_0. The coin is not biased.

Notice that since $p = 0.5$ the two tails are symmetrical and the value of c_2 could have been inferred from that of c_1.

(b) A type I error occurs when you reject H_0, and this occurs when $X \leqslant 5$ or $X \geqslant 15$.

$$P(\text{type I error}) = P(X \leqslant 5 \mid p = 0.5) + P(X \geqslant 15 \mid p = 0.5)$$
$$= 0.0207 + 0.0207$$
$$= 0.0414$$

(c) A type II error occurs when you do not have sufficient evidence to reject H_0 when H_1 is true. You do not have evidence to reject H_0 if $X > 6$ or $X < 14$.

$$P(\text{type II error}) = P(6 \leqslant X \leqslant 14 \mid p = 0.25)$$
$$= P(X \leqslant 14 \mid p = 0.25) - P(X \leqslant 5 \mid p = 0.25)$$
$$= 1 - 0.6172$$
$$= 0.3828$$

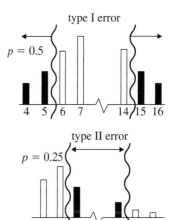

Exercise 1A

1 The random variable $X \sim N(\mu, 3^2)$. A random sample of 20 observations of X is taken, and the sample mean $\overline{X}$ is taken to be the test statistic. It is desired to test $H_0 : \mu = 50$ against $H_1 : \mu > 50$, using a 1% level of significance.
(a) Find the critical region for this test.
(b) State the probability of a type I error, and given that the true mean was later found to be 53, find the probability of a type II error.

2 The random variable $X \sim N(\mu, 2^2)$. A random sample of 16 observations of X is taken, and the sample mean $\overline{X}$ is taken to be the test statistic. It is desired to test $H_0 : \mu = 30$ against $H_1 : \mu < 30$, using a 5% level of significance.
(a) Find the critical region for this test.
(b) State the probability of a type I error and, given that the true mean was later found to be 28.5, find the probability of a type II error.

3 The random variable $X \sim \mathrm{N}(\mu, 4^2)$. A random sample of 25 observations of X is taken, and the sample mean $\overline{X}$ is taken to be the test statistic. It is desired to test $\mathrm{H}_0 : \mu = 40$ against $\mathrm{H}_1 : \mu \neq 40$, using a 1% level of significance.

(a) Find the critical region for this test.

(b) State the probability of a type I error and, given that the true mean was later found to be 42, find the probability of a type II error.

4 The random variable X is binomially distributed. A sample of 10 is taken, and it is desired to test $\mathrm{H}_0 : p = 0.25$ against $\mathrm{H}_1 : p > 0.25$, using a 5% level of significance.

(a) Calculate the critical region for this test.

(b) State the probability of a type I error and, given that the true value of p was later found to be 0.30, calculate the probability of a type II error.

5 The random variable X is binomially distributed. A sample of 20 is taken, and it is desired to test $\mathrm{H}_0 : p = 0.30$ against $\mathrm{H}_1 : p < 0.30$, using a 1% level of significance.

(a) Calculate the critical region for this test.

(b) State the probability of a type I error and, given that the true probability was later found to be 0.25, calculate the probability of a type II error.

6 The random variable X is binomially distributed. A sample of 10 is taken, and it is desired to test $\mathrm{H}_0 : p = 0.45$ against $\mathrm{H}_1 : p \neq 0.45$, using a 5% level of significance.

(a) Calculate the critical region for this test.

(b) State the probability of a type I error and, given that the true probability was later found to be 0.40, calculate the probability of a type II error.

7 The random variable X has a Poisson distribution. A sample is taken, and it is desired to test $\mathrm{H}_0 : \lambda = 6$ against $\mathrm{H}_1 : \lambda > 6$, using a 5% level of significance.

(a) Find the critical region for this test.

(b) Calculate the probability of a type I error and, given that the true value of λ was later found to be 7, calculate the probability of a type II error.

8 The random variable X has a Poisson distribution. A sample is taken, and it is desired to test $H_0 : \lambda = 4.5$ against $H_1 : \lambda < 4.5$, using a 5% level of significance.

(a) Find the critical region for this test.

(b) Calculate the probability of a type I error and, given that the true value of λ was later found to be 3.5, calculate the probability of a type II error.

9 The random variable X has a Poisson distribution. A sample is taken, and it is desired to test $H_0 : \lambda = 9$ against $H_1 : \lambda \neq 9$, using a 5% level of significance.

(a) Find the critical region for this test.

(b) Calculate the probability of a type I error and, given that the true value of λ was later found to be 8, calculate the probability of a type II error.

10 A manufacturer claims that the average outside diameter of a particular washer produced by his factory is 15 mm. The diameter is assumed to be normally distributed with a standard deviation of 1. The manufacturer decides to take a random sample of 25 washers from each day's production in order to monitor any changes in the mean diameter.

(a) Using a significance level of 5%, find the critical region to be used for this test.

(b) Assuming that the average diameter had in fact increased to 15.6 mm, find the probability that the day's production would be wrongly accepted.

11 The number of Petrie dishes that a laboratory technician can deal with in one hour can be modelled by a normal distribution with mean 40 and standard deviation 8. A producer of glass pipettes claims that a new type of pipette will speed up the rate at which the technician works.

A random sample of 30 technicians tried out the new pipettes and the average number of Petrie dishes they dealt with per hour, $\overline{X}$, was recorded.

(a) Using a 5% significance level, find the critical value of $\overline{X}$.

The average number of Petrie dishes dealt with per hour using the new pipettes was in fact 42.

(b) Find the probability of making a type II error.

The manufacturer of the pipettes would like to reduce the probability of a type II error being made and recommends that the significance level can be changed.

(c) What recommendation would you make and why?

1.4 The size and power of a test

You have already seen that a type I error occurs when the null hypothesis is rejected when it is in fact true. The probability of a type I error is written as α and is often known as the **size of the test**.

■ **The size of a test is the probability of rejecting the null hypothesis when it is in fact true, and this is equal to the probability of a type I error.**

When conducting a hypothesis test, you should also be interested in rejecting the null hypothesis when it is in fact untrue. The probability of rejecting the null hypothesis H_0 when it is untrue is known as the **power of the test**. You have already seen that a type II error occurs when the null hypothesis is not rejected when it is in fact untrue, and that the probability of this happening is written as β. Thus, calculating the probability of rejecting the null hypothesis when it is untrue is a simple process. Since P(rejecting H_0 when H_0 is untrue) + P(accepting H_0 when H_0 is untrue) has to add up to 1,

$$\text{Power} + \beta = 1$$

and

$$\text{Power} = 1 - \beta$$

■ **The power of a test is the probability of rejecting the null hypothesis when it is not true.**

■ **Power** $= 1 - \beta = 1 - $ **P(type II error)**
   $= $ **P(being in the critical region when H_1 is true)**

Clearly, as β increases the power decreases, and as β decreases the power increases. The higher the power of a test, the higher the probability of accepting H_1 when H_1 is true. It follows that the higher the power the better the test.

If the power is greater than 0.5, the probability of coming to the correct conclusion (accepting H_1 when H_1 is true) is greater than the probability of coming to the wrong conclusion (accepting H_0 when H_1 is true).

On page 6 you were told that, generally, if you increase the sample size the probability of a type II error decreases. It follows that the larger the sample size, the greater the power of the test. Increasing the sample size is preferable to reducing the significance level as a way of increasing the power of a test.

1.5 The power function

So far you have calculated the probability of a type II error only when you have been given a particular value of the population parameter of interest. Population parameters are seldom known, and as was pointed out earlier, if they were known there would be little point in doing the test anyway. Sometimes past experience can give you some idea of likely values of the parameters, but in general, since you do not know the value of the parameter, you cannot decide the power of the test concerned. However, it is possible in these cases to calculate the power as a function of the relevant parameter (which we shall generalise as θ). Such a function is known as a **power function**, and in this book Power(θ) will be used to represent the power function for the parameter θ.

■ **The power function, Power(θ), of a test is the function of the parameter θ which gives the probability that the sample point will fall in the critical region of the test if θ is the true value of the parameter.**

A power function enables you to calculate the power of the test for any given value of θ, and thus to plot a graph of power against θ.

Example 6

In a binomial experiment consisting of 10 trials the random variable X represents the number of successes and p the probability of a success.

In a test of $H_0 : p = 0.4$ against $H_1 : p > 0.4$, a critical region of $X \geqslant 8$ was used.

Find the power of this test when

(a) $p = 0.5$,
(b) $p = 0.8$.
(c) Comment on your results.

(a)
$$\begin{aligned}
\text{Power} &= P(X \geqslant 8 \mid p = 0.5) \\
&= 1 - P(X \leqslant 7 \mid p = 0.5) \\
&= 1 - 0.9453 \\
&= 0.0547
\end{aligned}$$

(b)
$$\begin{aligned}
\text{Power} &= P(X \geqslant 8 \mid p = 0.8) \\
&= P(X \leqslant 2 \mid p = 0.2) \\
&= 0.6778
\end{aligned}$$

(c) The test is more discriminating for larger values of p.

In this particular example you were able to use the tables to find these probabilities. If the values had not been in the tables (e.g. if n was 13) then you would have to calculate them using your knowledge of the binomial distribution. For $X \geqslant 8$, and $n = 10$, the calculation would be

$$
\begin{aligned}
\text{Power}(p) &= \frac{10!}{8!\,2!} p^8 (1-p)^2 + \frac{10!}{9!\,1!} p^9 (1-p) + \frac{10!}{10!} p^{10} \\
&= 45p^8 (1-p)^2 + 10p^9 (1-p) + p^{10} \\
&= 45p^8 (1 - 2p + p^2) + 10p^9 (1-p) + p^{10} \\
&= 45p^8 - 90p^9 + 45p^{10} + 10p^9 - 10p^{10} + p^{10} \\
&= 45p^8 - 80p^9 + 36p^{10}
\end{aligned}
$$

This is the power function.

Using this power function you can calculate the power function for any value of p.

Some resulting values are shown in the table below:

p	0	0.1	0.2	0.3	0.4	0.5	0.6	0.7	0.8	0.9	1.0
Power	0	0	0	0.0016	0.0123	0.0547	0.1673	0.3828	0.6778	0.9298	1

A graph may be drawn to show how the power varies as p changes. Such a graph is shown below.

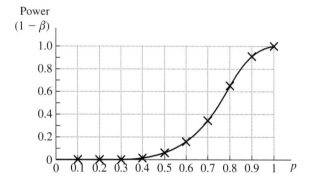

Example 7

Past experience has shown that the number of accidents that take place at a road junction has a Poisson distribution with an average of 3.5 accidents per month. A trading estate is built along one of the roads leading away from the junction and the local council is anxious that this may have increased the accident rate. To see whether the number of accidents has increased, a test is set up with the null hypothesis $H_0 : \lambda = 3.5$, and with the alternative hypothesis being accepted if the number of accidents, X, within the first month after the alteration was $\geqslant 7$.

(a) Find the size of the test.

(b) Find the power function for the test and sketch the graph of the power function.

(a) $$\text{Size of test} = P(X \geqslant 7 \mid \lambda = 3.5)$$
$$= 1 - P(X \leqslant 6 \mid \lambda = 3.5)$$
$$= 1 - 0.9347$$
$$= 0.0653$$

(b) $$\beta(\lambda) = P(X \leqslant 6 \mid \lambda > 3.5)$$

$$= e^{-\lambda} + \lambda e^{-\lambda} + \frac{\lambda^2}{2!}e^{-\lambda} + \frac{\lambda^3}{3!}e^{-\lambda} + \frac{\lambda^4}{4!}e^{-\lambda} + \frac{\lambda^5}{5!}e^{-\lambda} + \frac{\lambda^6}{6!}e^{-\lambda}$$

$$= e^{-\lambda}\left(1 + \lambda + \frac{\lambda^2}{2} + \frac{\lambda^3}{6} + \frac{\lambda^4}{24} + \frac{\lambda^5}{120} + \frac{\lambda^6}{720}\right)$$

Power $= 1 - \beta$

So the power function is given by

$$\text{Power}(\lambda) = 1 - e^{-\lambda}\left(1 + \lambda + \frac{\lambda^2}{2} + \frac{\lambda^3}{6} + \frac{\lambda^4}{24} + \frac{\lambda^5}{120} + \frac{\lambda^6}{720}\right)$$

This enables values of the power of the test to be calculated for different values of λ.

$$\lambda = 4 \text{ gives power} = 0.1107$$
$$\lambda = 5 \text{ gives power} = 0.2378$$
$$\lambda = 6 \text{ gives power} = 0.3937$$
$$\lambda = 7 \text{ gives power} = 0.5503$$
$$\lambda = 8 \text{ gives power} = 0.6866$$
$$\lambda = 9 \text{ gives power} = 0.7932$$
$$\lambda = 10 \text{ gives power} = 0.8699$$

The graph is shown below:

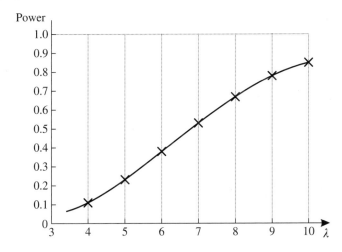

Example 8

A manufacturer of sweets supplies a mixed assortment of chocolates in a jar. He claims that 40% of the chocolates have a 'hard centre', the remainder being 'soft centred'.

A shopkeeper does not believe the manufacturer's claim and proposes to test it using the following hypotheses.

$$H_0 : p = 0.4 \quad H_1 : p < 0.4$$

where p is the proportion of 'hard centres' in the jar. Two tests are proposed.

In test A he takes a random sample of 10 chocolates from the jar and rejects H_0 if the number of 'hard centres' is fewer than 2.

(a) Find the size of test A.

(b) Show that the power function of test A is given by

$$(1 - p)^{10} + 10p(1 - p)^9$$

In test B he takes a random sample of 5 chocolates from the jar, and if there are no 'hard centres' he rejects H_0; otherwise he takes a second sample of 5 chocolates and H_0 is rejected if there are no further 'hard centres' on this second occasion.

(c) Find the size of test B.

(d) Find an expression for the power function of test B.

The power for test A and test B are given in the table for various values of p.

p	0.1	0.2	0.25	0.3	0.35
Power for test A	0.74	r	0.24	s	0.09
Power for test B	0.83	0.55	0.42	0.31	0.22

(e) Calculate the values of r and s.

(f) Suggest which of the two tests the shopkeeper should use.

(a) Size of test $A = P(X < 2)$
using Appendix, Table 1 (binomial cumulative function) with $p = 0.4$, $X < 2$ with probability 0.0464.

(b) Power of test $A = P(\text{Reject } H_0 \mid p)$
$$= P(X = 0 \mid p) + P(X = 1 \mid p)$$
$$= (1 - p)^{10} + 10p(1 - p)^9$$

(c) Size of test $B = P(\text{reject } H_0 \mid p = 0.4)$
$$= P(X = 0) + [1 - P(X = 0)]P(X = 0)$$
$$= 0.6^5 + (1 - 0.6^5) \times 0.6^5$$
$$= 0.1495$$

(d) Power of test B $= $ P(0 hard centres in first 5) $+$ P(0 hard
centres in second $5 \mid > 0$ hard centres in first 5)

$$= P(X = 0 \mid p) + [1 - P(X = 0 \mid p)]P(X = 0 \mid p)$$
$$= (1 - p)^5 + [1 - (1 - p)^5](1 - p)^5$$
$$= (1 - p)^5[1 + 1 - (1 - p)^5]$$
$$= (1 - p)^5[2 - (1 - p)^5]$$
$$= 2(1 - p)^5 - (1 - p)^{10}$$

(e) Test A: $p = 0.2$ Power $= (1 - 0.2)^{10} + 10(0.2)(1 - 0.2)^9$
$$= 0.38$$

so $r = 0.38$

$p = 0.3$ Power $= (1 - 0.3)^{10} + 10(0.3)(1 - 0.3)^9$

so $s = 0.15$

(f) Power for test B $>$ Power for test A for all values of p, so he
should use test B.

Exercise 1B

1 The random variable $X \sim N(\mu, 3^2)$. A random sample of 25
observations of X is taken and the sample mean $\overline{X}$ is taken as
the test statistic. It is desired to test $H_0 : \mu = 20$ against
$H_1 : \mu > 20$ using a 5% significance level.
(a) Find the critical region for this test.
(b) Given that $\mu = 20.8$ find the power of this test.

2 The random variable X is a binomial distribution. A sample of
20 is taken from it. It is desired to test $H_0 : p = 0.35$ against
$H_1 : p > 0.35$ using a 5% significance level.
(a) Calculate the size of this test.
(b) Given that $p = 0.30$ calculate the power of this test.

3 The random variable X has a Poisson distribution. A sample is
taken and it is desired to test $H_0 : \lambda = 4.5$ against $H_1 : \lambda < 4.5$.
If a 5% significance level is to be used:
(a) Find the size of this test.
(b) Given that $\lambda = 4.1$ find the power of the test.

4 A manufacturer claims that a particular rivet produced in his
factory has a diameter of 2 mm, and that the diameter is
normally distributed with a variance of 0.004 mm. A random

sample of 25 rivets is taken from a day's production and is to be tested to see whether the mean diameter has altered, up or down, from the stated figure. A 5% significance level is to be used for this test.

If the mean diameter had in fact altered to 2.02 mm, calculate the power of this test.

5 A single observation x is taken from a Poisson distribution with parameter λ. This observation is to be used to test $H_0 : \lambda = 6.5$ against $H_1 : \lambda < 6.5$. The critical region chosen was $x \leqslant 2$.
   (a) Find the size of the test.
   (b) Show that the power function of this test is given by $e^{-\lambda}(1 + \lambda + \frac{1}{2}\lambda^2)$.

   The table below gives the value of the power function to two decimal places.

λ	1	2	3	4	5	6
Power	0.92	s	0.42	0.24	t	0.06

   (c) Calculate values for s and t.
   (d) Draw a graph of the power function.
   (e) Find the values of λ for which the test is more likely than not to come to the correct conclusion.

6 In a binomial experiment consisting of 12 trials, X represents the number of successes and p the probability of a success.

   In a test of $H_0 : p = 0.45$ against $H_1 : p < 0.45$ the null hypothesis is rejected if the number of successes is 2 or less.
   (a) Find the size of this test.
   (b) Show that the power function for this test is given by $(1 - p)^{12} + 12p(1 - p)^{11} + 66p^2(1 - p)^{10}$.
   (c) Find the power of this test when p is 0.6.

1.6 The quality of estimators

You have often taken sample data and used it to find an estimate of the corresponding population parameter. For example, you might have used the sample mean $\overline{X}$ as an estimator of μ, or the sample variance S^2 as an estimator of σ^2. (You will recall that when using the 'hat' notation you would write $\hat{\mu}$ and $\hat{\sigma}^2$ for the estimates of μ and σ^2, that is, $\hat{\mu}$ instead of $\bar{x}$ and $\hat{\sigma}^2$ instead of s^2).

It would be surprising if the estimate based on the sample gave the true value of the population parameter, but you would expect the estimated value to be quite close to the true value. The questions you will investigate in this part of the chapter are 'How good are these estimates?' and 'What are the qualities of a good estimator?'.

Before starting on this section you should remind yourself of the following important properties of expected values and variances which were given in previous books.

$$E(aX) = aE(X)$$
$$E(X \pm Y) = E(X) \pm E(Y)$$
$$Var(aX) = a^2 Var(X)$$
$$Var(X \pm Y) = Var(X) + Var(Y) \text{ if } X \text{ and } Y \text{ are independent}$$

These formulae will be used throughout this section.

1.7 Unbiased estimators

Unbiased estimators were discussed in Chapter 3, pages 21 to 26 of Statistics 3.

When sampling from a population, the estimator obtained from the sample data will have a distribution even though the estimate has a specific value. This is because each time you take a different sample the value of the estimate will change. You found that when a simple random sample of size n was taken from a population with mean μ and variance σ^2, the mean $\bar{X}$ of the sample was such that $E(\bar{X}) = \mu$ and $Var(\bar{X}) = \dfrac{\sigma^2}{n}$. You will recall that $\dfrac{\sigma}{\sqrt{n}}$, the standard deviation of $\bar{X}$, is known as the standard error of the mean (or commonly just the standard error).

If you use the mean of the sample $\bar{X}$ as an estimator for μ then the value of $\bar{X}$ will vary each time you take a sample. If the population has a normal distribution then the distribution of $\bar{X}$ might appear as shown below.

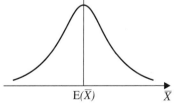

In the case where $\bar{X}$ is being used to estimate μ, the value of a particular estimate $\bar{x}$ may not equal μ, but you can have confidence in the estimate because $E(\bar{X}) = \mu$.

If you generalise the parameter being estimated as θ and the estimator as Y then one obvious requirement of any estimator Y is that the expectation of the estimator $E(Y)$ should equal the population parameter θ being estimated. Such an estimator is called unbiased. See Statistics 3, page 21.

■ **An estimator Y is an unbiased estimator of the population parameter θ if $E(Y) = \theta$.**

Example 9

The weights, in kg, of students just joining a college are normally distributed with a mean μ and variance σ^2. A random sample of 6 of these students was taken and the mean of this sample $\overline{X}$ was calculated.

(a) Show that $\overline{X}$ is an unbiased estimator of μ.

A second random sample of 4 of these students was taken and its mean was $\overline{Y}$.

(b) Show that

(i) $$\frac{\overline{X} + \overline{Y}}{2}$$

(ii) $$\frac{6\overline{X} + 4\overline{Y}}{10}$$

are both unbiased estimators of μ.

(a) $$E(\overline{X}) = \left(\frac{X_1 + X_2 + X_3 + X_4 + X_5 + X_6}{6}\right)$$
$$= \tfrac{1}{6}[E(X_1) + E(X_2) + E(X_3) + E(X_4) + E(X_5) + E(X_6)]$$
$$= \tfrac{1}{6}(\mu + \mu + \mu + \mu + \mu + \mu)$$
$$= \mu$$

(b) (i) $$E\left(\frac{\overline{X} + \overline{Y}}{2}\right) = \tfrac{1}{2}E(\overline{X}) + \tfrac{1}{2}E(\overline{Y})$$
$$= \tfrac{1}{2}\mu + \tfrac{1}{2}\mu$$
$$= \mu$$

(ii) $$E\left(\frac{6\overline{X} + 4\overline{Y}}{10}\right) = \tfrac{1}{10}[6E(\overline{X}) + 4E(\overline{Y})]$$
$$= \tfrac{1}{10}(6\mu + 4\mu)$$
$$= \mu$$

An estimator Y which has the property $E(Y) \neq \theta$ is called a **biased estimator**. The **bias** is simply the expected value of the estimator minus the parameter being estimated.

■ **If a statistic Y is used as an estimator for a population parameter θ then the bias $= E(Y) - \theta$.**

Notice that the bias will be positive if $E(Y) > \theta$, but negative if $E(Y) < \theta$. In practice you should always aim to use an unbiased statistic.

Example 10

Using the information from example 9,

(a) show that the estimator $\dfrac{\overline{X} + 2\overline{Y}}{2}$ is a biased estimator, and

(b) find the bias of the estimator.

(a)
$$\mathrm{E}\left(\frac{\overline{X} + 2\overline{Y}}{2}\right) = \tfrac{1}{2}[\mathrm{E}(\overline{X}) + 2\mathrm{E}(\overline{Y})]$$
$$= \tfrac{1}{2}(\mu + 2\mu)$$
$$= 1\tfrac{1}{2}\mu$$

Since $1\tfrac{1}{2}\mu \neq \mu$, $\dfrac{\overline{X} + 2\overline{Y}}{2}$ is a biased estimator.

(b)
$$\mathrm{Bias} = \mathrm{E}\left(\frac{\overline{X} + 2\overline{Y}}{2}\right) - \mu$$
$$= 1\tfrac{1}{2}\mu - \mu$$
$$= \tfrac{1}{2}\mu$$

Example 11

A sample of size n is taken from a population with a mean of μ and variance of σ^2.

(a) Show that the sample mean $\overline{X}$ is an unbiased estimator of μ.

(b) Show that as n increases $\mathrm{Var}(\overline{X})$ decreases.

(c) Show that $S^2 = \dfrac{\sum X_i^2 - n\overline{X}^2}{n-1}$ is an unbiased estimator of σ^2,

but that $Y = \dfrac{\sum X_i^2 - n\overline{X}^2}{n}$ is a biased estimator of σ^2.

(a)
$$\mathrm{E}(\overline{X}) = \mathrm{E}\left(\frac{X_1 + X_2 + \ldots + X_n}{n}\right)$$
$$= \frac{1}{n}[\mathrm{E}(X_1) + \mathrm{E}(X_2) + \ldots + \mathrm{E}(X_n)]$$
$$= \frac{1}{n}(\mu + \mu + \ldots + \mu)$$
$$= \mu$$

(b)
$$\mathrm{Var}(\overline{X}) = \mathrm{Var}\left(\frac{X_1 + X_2 + \ldots + X_n}{n}\right)$$
$$= \frac{1}{n^2}[\mathrm{Var}(X_1) + \mathrm{Var}(X_2) + \ldots + \mathrm{Var}(X_n)]$$
$$= \frac{1}{n^2}(\sigma^2 + \sigma^2 + \ldots + \sigma^2)$$
$$= \frac{1}{n}\sigma^2$$

As n increases $\dfrac{1}{n}$ decreases so $\mathrm{Var}(\overline{X})$ will also decrease.

(c)
$$E(S^2) = E\left(\frac{\sum X_i^2 - n\bar{X}^2}{n-1}\right)$$

$$= \frac{1}{(n-1)} E\left(\sum X_i^2 - n\bar{X}^2\right)$$

$$= \frac{1}{(n-1)}\left[\sum E(X_i^2) - nE(\bar{X}^2)\right]$$

Now $\mathrm{Var}(X) = E(X^2) - [E(X)]^2$

so
$$E(X_i^2) = \mathrm{Var}(X) + [E(X)]^2$$
$$= \sigma^2 + \mu^2$$

and
$$\sum E(X_i^2) = n\sigma^2 + n\mu^2$$

also
$$E(\bar{X}^2) = \mathrm{Var}(\bar{X}) + [E(\bar{X})]^2$$
$$= \frac{1}{n}\sigma^2 + \mu^2$$

so
$$nE(\bar{X}^2) = \sigma^2 + n\mu^2$$

Thus
$$E(S^2) = \frac{1}{(n-1)}(n\sigma^2 + n\mu^2 - \sigma^2 - n\mu^2)$$
$$= \sigma^2$$

Thus S^2 is an unbiased estimator of σ^2.

If $n-1$ is replaced by n in the above calculation you get

$$E(Y) = \frac{1}{n}(n\sigma^2 + n\mu^2 - \sigma^2 - n\mu^2)$$

$$= \frac{n-1}{n}\sigma^2$$

so Y is a biased estimator of σ^2. The bias of Y will be $-\frac{1}{n}\sigma^2$.

1.8 Efficient estimators

In example 9 you had three different estimators, each of which was unbiased. Which is the best (or most efficient) one to use?

In Statistics 1 you learnt that there were two measures that could be used to describe a distribution – the mean, which is a measure of location or position, and the variance, which is a measure of dispersion or spread. Two unbiased estimators of the population mean μ having different variances are shown in the following diagram.

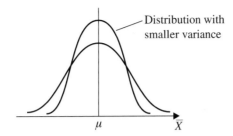

Distribution with smaller variance

μ $\overline{X}$

You can see from the diagram that the distribution with the smaller variance has its values clustered closer to the mean value μ (this is what you mean when you say its variance is smaller). Thus any estimate $\bar{x}$ is likely to be closer to $E(\overline{X})$. The estimator with the smaller variance is said to be the more efficient.

■ **If U and V are two unbiased estimators of θ with $\mathrm{Var}(U) < \mathrm{Var}(V)$ then U is the more efficient.**

Example 12

A random sample of size 3 is taken, without replacement, from a population with mean μ and variance σ^2. Two unbiased estimators of the mean of the population are $\hat{\mu}_1 = \frac{1}{3}(X_1 + X_2 + X_3)$ and $\hat{\mu}_2 = \frac{1}{4}(X_1 + 2X_2 + X_3)$.

(a) Calculate $\mathrm{Var}(\hat{\mu}_1)$ and $\mathrm{Var}(\hat{\mu}_2)$.
(b) Hence state, giving a reason, which estimator you would recommend.   [E]

(a) $\mathrm{Var}(\hat{\mu}_1) = \frac{1}{9}[\mathrm{Var}(X_1) + \mathrm{Var}(X_2) + \mathrm{Var}(X_3)]$

$= \frac{1}{9}(\sigma^2 + \sigma^2 + \sigma^2)$

$= \frac{1}{9}(3\sigma^2)$

$= \frac{\sigma^2}{3}$

$\mathrm{Var}(\hat{\mu}_2) = \frac{1}{16}[\mathrm{Var}(X_1) + 4\mathrm{Var}(X_2) + \mathrm{Var}(X_3)]$

$= \frac{1}{16}(\sigma^2 + 4\sigma^2 + \sigma^2)$

$= \frac{3\sigma^2}{8}$

(b) You would use $\hat{\mu}_1$ since this has the smaller variance.

Example 13

Find the most efficient estimator of those defined in example 9.

$$\text{Var}(\overline{X}) = \text{Var}\left(\frac{X_1 + X_2 + X_3 + X_4 + X_5 + X_6}{6}\right)$$

$$= \tfrac{1}{36}[\text{Var}(X_1) + \text{Var}(X_2) + \text{Var}(X_3) + \text{Var}(X_4) + \text{Var}(X_5) + \text{Var}(X_6)]$$

$$= \tfrac{1}{36}(\sigma^2 + \sigma^2 + \sigma^2 + \sigma^2 + \sigma^2 + \sigma^2)$$

$$= \tfrac{1}{6}\sigma^2$$

$$\text{Var}\left(\frac{\overline{X} + \overline{Y}}{2}\right) = \tfrac{1}{4}[\text{Var}(\overline{X}) + \text{Var}(\overline{Y})]$$

$$= \tfrac{1}{4}\left(\tfrac{1}{6}\sigma^2 + \tfrac{1}{4}\sigma^2\right)$$

$$= \tfrac{5}{48}\sigma^2$$

$$\text{Var}\left(\frac{6\overline{X} + 4\overline{Y}}{10}\right) = \tfrac{1}{100}[36\text{Var}(\overline{X}) + 16\text{Var}(\overline{Y})]$$

$$= \tfrac{1}{100}\left[36\left(\tfrac{1}{6}\sigma^2\right) + 16\left(\tfrac{1}{4}\sigma^2\right)\right]$$

$$= \tfrac{1}{10}\sigma^2$$

The most efficient estimator is $\dfrac{6\overline{X} + 4\overline{Y}}{10}$, since it has the smallest variance.

1.9 Consistent estimators

In example 11 it was shown that the sample mean $\overline{X}$ was an unbiased estimator of μ, and that as n increases the variance of this estimator decreases. This is a property that makes $\overline{X}$ a very useful estimator of μ. By increasing the sample size it is possible to make sure that the values of any estimates should be closer to the value of μ. If an unbiased estimator has the property that its variance approaches zero as n approaches infinity, it is known as a **consistent** estimator. Sometimes an estimator, Y, may be asymptotically unbiased. This means that $\text{E}(Y) \rightarrow \theta$ as $n \rightarrow \infty$. Such an estimate is also called consistent if $\text{Var}(Y) \rightarrow 0$ as $n \rightarrow \infty$.

■ **If Y is an unbiased (or asymptotically unbiased) estimator for an unknown parameter θ, then Y is a consistent estimator for θ if $\text{E}(Y) = \theta$ and $\text{Var}(Y) \rightarrow 0$ as $n \rightarrow \infty$, where n is the size of the sample from which Y is obtained.**

Example 14

A sample of size n is taken from a population that has a mean of μ and a variance of σ^2.

Show that the sample mean $\bar{X}$ is a consistent estimator of μ.

From example 11, $\mathrm{Var}(\bar{X}) = \dfrac{\sigma^2}{n}$.

As $n \to \infty$, $\dfrac{\sigma^2}{n} \to 0$, so $\bar{X}$ is a consistent estimator of μ.

Example 15

From a binomial population in which the proportion of successes is p, a random sample of size n is taken and the number of successes X is recorded. The proportion of successes in the sample, R, is used as an estimator for p. Show that R is an unbiased and consistent estimator of p.

$$\mathrm{E}(R) = \mathrm{E}\left(\frac{X}{n}\right)$$

$$= \frac{1}{n}\mathrm{E}(X)$$

$$= \frac{1}{n}(np)$$

$$= p$$

so R is an unbiased estimator of p.

$$\mathrm{Var}(R) = \mathrm{Var}\left(\frac{X}{n}\right)$$

$$= \frac{1}{n^2}\mathrm{Var}(X)$$

$$= \frac{1}{n^2}[np(1-p)]$$

$$= \frac{1}{n}p(1-p)$$

Thus as $n \to \infty$, $\mathrm{Var}(R) \to 0$ and R is a consistent estimator.

Example 16

A bag is known to contain red and yellow balls. In order to find the proportion, p, of red balls in the bag, a sample of m balls is taken. There were X red balls in the sample.

It was suggested that a sample of m was rather small, so the balls were returned to the bag and a second sample of n balls was taken. There were Y red balls in this sample.

Possible estimators for p are

$$R_1 = \tfrac{1}{2}\left(\frac{X}{m} + \frac{2Y}{n}\right)$$

$$R_2 = \tfrac{1}{2}\left(\frac{X}{m} + \frac{Y}{n}\right)$$

and

$$R_3 = \frac{X + Y}{m + n}$$

(a) Show that R_1 is a biased estimator of p and calculate the bias of R_1.

(b) Show that R_2 and R_3 are unbiased estimators of p.

(c) Find the variances of R_2 and R_3.

(d) If $m = 10$ and $n = 20$ state, giving reasons, which estimator you would choose.

(a)

$$E(R_1) = E\left[\tfrac{1}{2}\left(\frac{X}{m} + \frac{2Y}{n}\right)\right]$$

$$= \tfrac{1}{2}\left[E\left(\frac{X}{m}\right) + 2E\left(\frac{Y}{n}\right)\right]$$

$$= \tfrac{1}{2}\left(\frac{mp}{m} + 2\frac{np}{n}\right)$$

$$= 1\tfrac{1}{2}p$$

$$\text{Bias} = E(R_1) - p = \tfrac{1}{2}p$$

(b)

$$E(R_2) = E\left[\tfrac{1}{2}\left(\frac{X}{m} + \frac{Y}{n}\right)\right]$$

$$= \tfrac{1}{2}\left\{\frac{1}{m}E(X) + \frac{1}{n}E(Y)\right\}$$

$$= \tfrac{1}{2}\left(\frac{mp}{m} + \frac{np}{n}\right)$$

$$= p$$

$$E(R_3) = \frac{1}{m + n}[E(X) + E(Y)]$$

$$= \frac{1}{m + n}(mp + np)$$

$$= p$$

(c)

$$\text{Var}(R_2) = \text{Var}\left[\tfrac{1}{2}\left(\frac{X}{m} + \frac{Y}{n}\right)\right]$$

$$= \tfrac{1}{4}\left\{\frac{1}{m^2}\text{Var}(X) + \frac{1}{n^2}\text{Var}(Y)\right\}$$

$$= \tfrac{1}{4}\left\{\frac{1}{m^2}mp(1 - p) + \frac{1}{n^2}np(1 - p)\right\}$$

$$= \tfrac{1}{4}p(1 - p)\left(\frac{m + n}{mn}\right)$$

$$\mathrm{Var}(R_3) = \frac{1}{(m+n)^2}[\mathrm{Var}(X) + \mathrm{Var}(Y)]$$

$$= \frac{1}{(m+n)^2}[mp(1-p) + np(1-p)]$$

$$= \frac{1}{m+n}p(1-p)$$

(d) Since R_1 is biased you only need to consider R_2 and R_3.
If $m = 10$ and $n = 20$

$$\mathrm{Var}(R_2) = \tfrac{1}{4}p(1-p)\left(\frac{20+10}{200}\right) = \tfrac{3}{80}p(1-p)$$

$$\mathrm{Var}(R_3) = \frac{1}{m+n}p(1-p) = \tfrac{1}{30}p(1-p)$$

$\mathrm{Var}(R_3) < \mathrm{Var}(R_2)$ so R_3 is the more efficient estimator.

Exercise 1C ○

1 If X_1, X_2, X_3, is a random sample from a population with
mean μ and variance σ^2, find which of the following
estimators of μ are unbiased. If any are biased find an
expression for the bias.
(a) $\tfrac{1}{8}X_1 + \tfrac{3}{8}X_2 + \tfrac{1}{2}X_3$ (b) $\tfrac{1}{4}X_1 + \tfrac{1}{2}X_2$
(c) $\tfrac{1}{3}X_1 + \tfrac{2}{3}X_2$ (d) $\tfrac{1}{3}(X_1 + X_2 + X_3)$
(e) $\tfrac{1}{5}X_1 + \tfrac{2}{5}X_2 + \tfrac{3}{5}X_3$

2 Find which one of the estimators in question 1 is the most
efficient.

3 If a random sample $X_1, X_2, X_3, \ldots, X_n$, is taken from a
population with mean μ and standard deviation σ, show that both

(a) $\dfrac{1}{n}(X_1 + X_2 + \ldots + X_{n-1} + X_n)$, and

(b) $2\dfrac{(nX_1 + (n-1)X_2 + \ldots + 2X_{n-1} + 1X_n)}{n(n+1)}$

are unbiased and consistent estimators for μ.

> You may use
>
> $\displaystyle\sum_{r=1}^{n} r = \tfrac{1}{2}n(n+1)$ and
>
> $\displaystyle\sum_{r=1}^{n} r^2 = \tfrac{1}{6}n(n+1)(2n+1)$

4 A uniform distribution on the interval $[0, a]$ has a mean of $\dfrac{a}{2}$,
and a variance of $\dfrac{a^2}{12}$. Three single samples X_1, X_2 and X_3 are
taken from this distribution, and are to be used to estimate a.

The following estimators are proposed.

(i) $X_1 + X_2 + X_3$

(ii) $\frac{2}{3}(X_1 + X_2 + X_3)$

(iii) $2(X_1 + 2X_2 + X_3)$

(a) Determine the bias, if any, of each of these estimators.

(b) Find the variance of each of these estimators.

(c) State, giving reasons, which of these estimators you would use.

(d) If $X_1 = 2$, $X_2 = 2.5$ and $X_3 = 3.2$, calculate the best estimate of a.

5   A bag contains 100 counters of which an unknown number m are blue. It is known that $2 \leqslant m \leqslant 98$. Two discs are drawn simultaneously from the bag and the number n of blue ones counted. It is desired to estimate m by $\hat{m} = cn$ where c is an unknown constant. Find the value of c given that the estimate is unbiased.

6   When a die is rolled the probability of obtaining a six is an unknown constant p. In order to estimate p the die is rolled n times and the number, X, of sixes is recorded. A second trial is then done with the die being rolled the same number of times, and the number of sixes, Y, is again recorded. Show that

(a) $\hat{p}_1 = \dfrac{3\overline{X} + 4\overline{Y}}{7n}$ and $\hat{p}_2 = \dfrac{\overline{X} + \overline{Y}}{2n}$ are unbiased and consistent

estimators of p.

(b) State, giving reasons, which of the two estimators is the better one.

7   A six-sided die has some of its faces showing the number 0 and the rest showing the number 1, so that p is the probability of getting a 1 when the die is thrown and q is the probability of getting a 0. If the random variable X is the value showing when the die is rolled,

(a) find $E(X)$ and $Var(X)$.

A random sample is now taken by rolling the die three times in order to get an estimate for p.

(b) Show that if $a_2X_1 + a_2X_2 + a_3X_3$ is to be an unbiased estimator of p then $a_1 + a_2 + a_3 = 1$.

(c) Find the variance of this estimator.

The following estimators of p are proposed.

(i) $\frac{1}{5}X_1 + \frac{2}{5}X_2 + \frac{2}{5}X_3$

(ii) $\frac{1}{4}X_1 + \frac{3}{8}X_2 + \frac{1}{4}X_3$

(iii) $\frac{4}{9}X_1 + \frac{5}{9}X_3$

(d) Find which of these is the best unbiased estimator.

SUMMARY OF KEY POINTS

1 A **type I error** occurs when H_0 is rejected when it is true.

2 The **probability of a type I error** (α) is the probability of obtaining a value of the test statistic within the critical region. This is sometimes called the size of the test.
For a continuous distribution

$$P(\text{type I error}) = \text{significance level of test}$$

3 A **type II error** occurs when H_0 is accepted when it is false.

4 The **probability of a type II error** (β) is the probability of obtaining a value of the test statistic that does not lie in the critical region assuming that H_1 is true.

5 The **power of a test** is the probability of rejecting H_0 when it is not true.

$$\text{Power} = 1 - \beta$$

6 The **power function**, Power(θ), of a test is the function of the parameter θ which gives the probability that the sample point will fall in the critical region of the test if θ is the true value of the population parameter.

7 An estimator Y is an **unbiased estimator** of the population parameter θ if $E(Y) = \theta$.
If an estimator Y is biased then the **bias** is given by $E(Y) - \theta$.

8 If there are two or more unbiased estimators of a population parameter θ then the **most efficient** is the one with the smallest variance.

9 If Y is an unbiased (or asymptotically unbiased) estimator of an unknown population parameter θ, then Y is a **consistent estimator** for θ if $E(Y) = \theta$ and $\text{Var}(Y) \to 0$ as $n \to \infty$, where n is the size of the sample from which Y is obtained.

One-sample procedures

2

This chapter extends the work done in Statistics 3 on hypothesis testing and confidence intervals when the sample taken is a single sample of size n. First we will consider the hypothesis test and confidence interval for the mean of a normal distribution when the variance is unknown and the sample size is small. Next we will develop a test and confidence interval for the variance. We begin by looking at a particular problem.

A shopkeeper sells jars of jam. The weights of the jars of jam are normally distributed with a mean of 150 g. A customer complains that the mean weight of the 8 jars of jam she had bought was only 147 g. An estimate for the variance of the weights of the 8 jars of jam calculated from the 8 observations was 2 g. Does she have cause for complaint or was she just unlucky?

In Statistics 3 you saw that if n observations were taken from a $N(\mu, \sigma^2)$ distribution, the sample mean $\overline{X}$ followed a $N\left(\mu, \dfrac{\sigma^2}{n}\right)$ distribution, and that

$$Z = \frac{(\overline{X} - \mu)}{\dfrac{\sigma}{\sqrt{n}}} \sim N(0, 1^2)$$

If, as in the case above, σ^2 is unknown, then S^2, an unbiased estimator of σ^2, can be used, where

$$S^2 = \frac{\sum\limits_{i=1}^{n} X_i^2 - n\overline{X}^2}{n - 1} = \frac{1}{n - 1}\left(\sum\limits_{i=1}^{n} X_i^2 - \frac{\left(\sum\limits_{i=1}^{n} X_i\right)^2}{n}\right)$$

> The limits and subscripts will often be omitted when it is obvious what is being summed over.

Then *providing **n** was large*,

$$\frac{(\overline{X} - \mu)}{\dfrac{S}{\sqrt{n}}} \approx N(0, 1^2)$$

In either case, if n was large, the shopkeeper's problem would have been solved by testing the null hypothesis $H_0 : \mu = 150$ against the alternative hypothesis $H_1 : \mu < 150$, by finding the critical region for Z and comparing it with the actual value z obtained from the sample.

In the shopkeeper's case, σ is unknown but the sample size is very small, and if you were to approximate $\dfrac{(\overline{X} - \mu)}{\dfrac{\sigma}{\sqrt{n}}}$ by $\dfrac{(\overline{X} - \mu)}{\dfrac{S}{\sqrt{n}}}$ the error could be rather large. You need to investigate further the distribution of $\dfrac{(\overline{X} - \mu)}{\dfrac{S}{\sqrt{n}}}$. We begin by looking at Student's t-distribution.

2.1 Student's *t*-distribution

The expression $\dfrac{(\overline{X} - \mu)}{\dfrac{S}{\sqrt{n}}}$ is usually represented by t. You should note that it is usual to use t for both the distribution and for a particular value of it, although some books use T for the random variable and t for a particular value of it. Usually it will be clear from the situation which one is being referred to.

W. S. Gosset, who published his works under the pseudonym 'the Student', first investigated the probability distribution of $\dfrac{(\overline{X} - \mu)}{\dfrac{S}{\sqrt{n}}}$ when the sample had been taken *from a normal distribution*. The resulting distribution is known as 'Student's t-distribution', or more commonly just the t-distribution.

Since the accuracy of S as an estimator of σ depends upon $(n-1)$ there is a whole family of t-distributions, one for each value of $(n-1)$.

You will recall that if a sample of size n is taken and there is only one constraint, the number of degrees of freedom $v = (n-1)$. To distinguish one distribution from another it is usual to talk about 'a t-distribution with v degrees of freedom' or for short 'the t_v-distribution'.

The t_v-distribution is symmetrical about zero, and as $v \to \infty$, $t_v \to N(0, 1^2)$. (This is why for large n you could use z as an approximation for t.) For smaller values of v, the curve is much flatter, as can be seen from the diagram below.

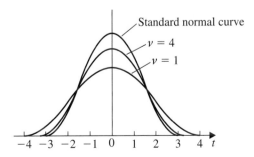

Tables of the *t*-distribution

Since the use of the *t*-distribution is confined to problems in which you wish to find the value of *t* which is exceeded with a certain probability, the table gives values of *t* that are exceeded with probabilities of 0.1, 0.05, 0.025, 0.01 and 0.005 (10%, 5%, 2.5%, 1% and 0.5%). This is done for a range of different *t*-distributions, each of which is identified by the value of its parameter *v*. You should make yourself familiar with the table (Appendix, Table 6, page 124). A brief extract from the top of the table is shown below.

The values in the table are those which a random variable with Student's *t*-distribution on *v* degrees of freedom exceeds with the probability shown.

v	0.10	0.05	0.025	0.01	0.005
1	3.078	6.314	12.706	31.821	63.657
2	1.886	2.920	4.303	6.965	9.925
3	1.638	2.353	3.182	4.541	5.841
4	1.533	2.132	2.776	3.747	4.604
5	1.476	2.015	2.571	3.365	4.032
6	1.440	1.943	2.447	3.143	3.707
7	1.415	1.895	2.365	2.998	3.499
8	1.397	1.860	2.306	2.896	3.355
9	1.383	1.833	2.262	2.821	3.250
10	1.372	1.812	2.228	2.764	3.169

Notice that different values of v ($n-1$, remember) are down the left-hand column, and the probabilities across the top. To find, for example, the value of *t* that is exceeded with a probability of 0.05 if $n = 8$, $v = 7$ (the critical value which we shall write as $t_7(0.05)$), you find the intersection of the $v = 7$ row and the probability $= 0.05$ column and read off $t_7(0.05) = 1.895$. The probability that the value of $t < 1.895$ is of course $1 - 0.05 = 0.95$, and by symmetry the probability that the value of $t < -1.895$ will be 0.05. For values of $v > 30$ you may have to go to the nearest value, since the table increases in steps of 2 from 30 to 40, in steps of 5 from 40 to 60, and then in steps of 10 up to 120. For larger values the normal distribution may be safely used.

When working with the *t*-distribution you are strongly advised to draw an appropriate diagram so that you are sure in your own mind which areas under the *t*-distribution you are dealing with.

Example 1

The random variable X has a t-distribution with 10 degrees of freedom. Determine values of t for which

(a) $P(X > t) = 0.025$,
(b) $P(X < t) = 0.95$,
(c) $P(X < t) = 0.025$,
(d) $P(|X| > t) = 0.05$,
(e) $P(|X| < t) = 0.98$.

(a) $v = 10$

> Note $|X|$ means the modulus of X. This is the absolute value of X ignoring the sign, e.g. the modulus of -5, written $|-5|$, is 5. So
> $$P(|X| > t) = P(X < -t) + P(X > t)$$
> $$P(|X| < t) = P(-t < X < t)$$

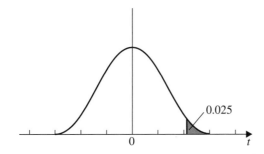

From the intersection of the 0.025 column and the $v = 10$ row, $t_{10}(0.025) = 2.228$.

(b)

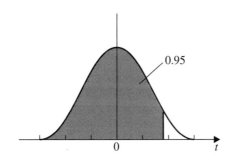

If $P(X < t) = 0.95$ then $P(X > t) = 1 - 0.95 = 0.05$.
From the table $t_{10}(0.05) = 1.812$.

(c)

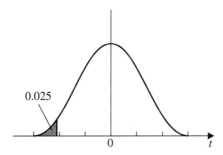

From (a), $P(X > t) = 0.025$ when $t = 2.228$, so by symmetry $P(X < t) = 0.025$ if $t = -2.228$.

(d)

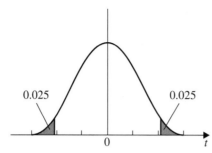

This is two sided, with probability of 0.025 at each tail. From (a) and (c):

$$P(|X| > t) = 0.05 \text{ if } X < -2.228 \text{ or } X > 2.228.$$

There are therefore 2 values for t and they are -2.228 and 2.228.

(e)

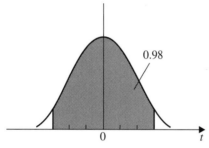

Again, a two-tailed problem. From the diagram you can see that you are looking for tails each with probability 0.01.

$P(|X| > t) = 0.01$ if $t = 2.764$, and $-2.764 < X < 2.764$.

Again there are 2 values of t; they are -2.764 and 2.764.

Example 2

The random variable Y has a t_4-distribution. Determine

(a) $P(Y > 3.747)$,
(b) $P(Y < -2.132)$.

(a) $v = 4$
From the $v = 4$ row of the table you can see that 3.747 is in the 0.01 probability column, so

$$P(Y > 3.747) = 0.01.$$

(b) From the $v = 4$ row of the table you can see that 2.132 is in the 0.05 probability column, so

$$P(Y > 2.132) = 0.05.$$

By symmetry $P(Y < -2.132) = 0.05$.

2.2 Hypothesis testing for the mean of a normal distribution with unknown variance

The following result, proved by W.S. Gossett, is very useful when hypothesis testing for the mean of a normal distribution. It allows you to use a t-distribution to find the critical region.

■ **If a random sample $X_1, X_2, \ldots, X_n$ is selected from a normal distribution with mean μ and unknown variance σ^2 then**

$$t = \frac{(\bar{X} - \mu)}{\frac{S}{\sqrt{n}}} \text{ has a } t_{n-1}\text{-distribution}$$

where

$$S^2 = \frac{\sum X_i^2 - n\bar{X}^2}{n - 1}$$

Apart from using the t-distribution rather than the normal distribution for finding the critical region, testing the mean of a normal distribution with unknown variance follows the same steps as you used when testing the mean of a normal distribution with known variance.

The following steps might help you in answering questions about hypothesis testing of the mean of a normal distribution with unknown variance.

1. Write down H_0.
2. Write down H_1.
3. Specify the significance level α.
4. Write down the number of degrees of freedom v.
5. Write down the critical region.
6. Calculate $\bar{x}$, s^2 and t.

$$\bar{x} = \sum \frac{x}{n}$$

$$s^2 = \frac{1}{n-1} \left[\sum x^2 - \frac{(\sum x)^2}{n} \right]$$

or $\quad s^2 = \dfrac{\sum x^2 - n\bar{x}^2}{n - 1}$

$$t = \frac{\bar{x} - \mu}{\frac{s}{\sqrt{n}}}$$

7. Conclusions.
   The following points should be addressed:
   (a) is the result significant or not?
   (b) what are the implications in terms of the original problem?

Let's apply these steps to the shopkeeper's problem at the beginning of this chapter:

A shopkeeper sells jars of jam. The weights of the jars of jam are normally distributed with a mean of 150 g. A customer complains that the mean weight of the 8 jars she had bought was only 147 g. An estimate for the standard deviation of the weights of the 8 jars of jam calculated from the 8 observations was 2 g. Does she have cause for complaint or was she just unlucky?

1. $H_0 : \mu = 150$

2. $H_1 : \mu < 150$

3. Significance level = 0.05 (one-tailed test).

4. $v = 8 - 1 = 7$.

5. From tables the critical value t_7 is -1.895 so the critical region is $t \leqslant -1.895$.

6. $\bar{x} = 147$, $\mu = 150$, $s = 2$.

$$t = \frac{\bar{x} - \mu}{\frac{s}{\sqrt{n}}} = \frac{147 - 150}{\frac{2}{\sqrt{8}}} = -4.2426$$

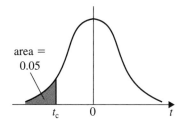

7. Now -4.2426 lies in the critical region, so the result is significant and H_0 is rejected. There is evidence to suggest that the mean weight is less than 150 g and the customer does have cause for complaint.

Example 3

The temperatures (°C) at noon were measured on 10 days during the month of March in West Cumbria. The readings were:

$$12.8 \quad 11.4 \quad 12.9 \quad 15.1 \quad 15.4$$
$$13.5 \quad 14.9 \quad 15.0 \quad 16.0 \quad 15.8$$

Using a 5% significance level, test whether or not there has been an increase over the previous year when the average noon temperature was 13.5 °C.

$H_0 : \mu = 13.5$

$H_1 : \mu > 13.5$

Significance level 5%

$v = 9$

From the table the critical value is $t_9 = 1.833$, so the critical region is $t \geqslant 1.833$.

$$\bar{x} = \frac{12.8 + 11.4 + 12.9 + 15.1 + 15.4 + 13.5 + 14.9 + 15.0 + 16.0 + 15.8}{10}$$

$$= 14.28$$

$$s^2 = \frac{\sum x^2 - n\bar{x}^2}{n - 1} = \frac{2060.28 - 10 \times (14.28)^2}{10 - 1} = 2.344$$

$$s = 1.531$$

Note that both of these can easily be read off directly from your calculator using the $\bar{x}$ and σ_{n-1} buttons.

$$t = \frac{\bar{x} - \mu}{\frac{s}{\sqrt{n}}} = \frac{14.28 - 13.5}{\frac{1.531}{\sqrt{10}}} = 1.611$$

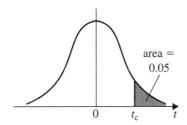

1.611 is not in the critical region so the result is not significant. There is insufficient evidence to suggest that the average temperature has increased.

Example 4

A concrete manufacturer tests cubes of its concrete at regular intervals, and their compressive strengths in $N\,m^{-1}$ are determined. The mean value of the strengths is required to be $0.47\,N\,m^{-1}$. A new supplier of cement offers to supply the firm at a cheaper rate than the present supplier, and a trial bag of cement is used to make 12 concrete cubes. Upon testing, these cubes are found to have strengths (x) such that $\sum x = 5.52$ and $\sum x^2 = 2.542$. Assume that the strengths are normally distributed.

(a) Stating your hypotheses clearly, test, at the 5% level of significance, whether or not the use of the new cement has altered the mean strength of the concrete.

In the light of your conclusion to test (a),

(b) what would you recommend the manufacturer to do?

(a) $H_0 : \mu = 0.47$

$H_1 : \mu \neq 0.47$

$v = 12 - 1 = 11$

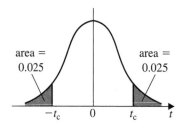

area = 0.025

area = 0.025

$-t_c$ 0 t_c t

From tables the critical value (remember to use 0.025 significance level since it is a two-tailed test) is 2.201. The critical region is $|t| \geqslant 2.201$.

$$\bar{x} = \frac{\sum x}{n} = \frac{5.52}{12} = 0.46 \, \mathrm{N \, m^{-1}}$$

$$s^2 = \frac{\sum x^2 - n\bar{x}^2}{n-1} = \frac{2.542 - (12 \times 0.46^2)}{11} = 0.000\,254\,5$$

$$s = 0.015\,95\ldots$$

$$t = \frac{\bar{x} - \mu}{\dfrac{s}{\sqrt{n}}} = \frac{0.46 - 0.47}{\dfrac{0.015\,95\ldots}{\sqrt{12}}} = -2.171$$

Now $|-2.171| < |-2.201|$

The result is not in the critical region. There is not enough evidence to suggest that the mean strength has altered.

(b) It seems that, since the mean strength has not altered, the manufacturer should accept the new supplier because he is cheaper. The two values -2.171 and -2.201 are quite close, however, and a one-tailed test of whether or not the strength has decreased should be done, or failing this a further sample could be taken.

Exercise 2A

1 Given that the random variable X has a t_{12}-distribution, find values of t such that

(a) $P(X < t) = 0.025$,

(b) $P(X > t) = 0.05$,

(c) $P(|X| > t) = 0.95$.

2 Given that the random variable X has a t_{26}-distribution, find

(a) $t_v(0.01)$,

(b) $t_v(0.05)$.

3 The random variable Y has a t_v-distribution. Find a value (or values) of t in each of the following:

(a) $v = 10$, $P(Y < t) = 0.95$,

(b) $v = 32$, $P(Y < t) = 0.005$,

(c) $v = 5$, $P(Y < t) = 0.025$,

(d) $v = 16$, $P(|Y| < t) = 0.98$,

(e) $v = 18$, $P(|Y| > t) = 0.10$.

4 Given that the observations 9, 11, 11, 12, 14, have been drawn from a normal distribution, test $H_0 : \mu = 11$ against $H_1 : \mu > 11$. Use a 5% significance level.

5 A random sample of size 28 taken from a normal distribution gave the following sample values: $\bar{x} = 17.1$ and $s^2 = 4$. Test $H_0 : \mu = 19$ against $H_1 : \mu < 19$. Use a 1% level of significance.

6 A random sample of size 13 taken from a normal distribution gave the following sample values: $\bar{x} = 3.26$, $s^2 = 0.64$. Test $H_0 : \mu = 3$ against $H_1 : \mu \neq 3$. Use a 5% significance level.

7 A certain brand of blanched hazelnuts for use in cooking is sold in packets. The weights of the packets of hazelnuts follow a normal distribution with mean μ. The manufacturer claims that $\mu = 100$ g. A sample of 15 packets is taken and the weight x of each is measured. The results are summarised by the following statistics:

$$\sum x = 1473, \sum x^2 = 148\,119$$

Test at the 5% significance level whether or not there is evidence to justify the manufacturer's claim.

8 A manufacturer claims that the lifetimes of its 100 watt bulbs have a mean of 1000 hours. A laboratory tests 8 bulbs and finds their lifetimes to be 985, 920, 1110, 1040, 945, 1165, 1170 and 1055 hours.

Stating your hypotheses clearly, examine whether or not the bulbs have a longer mean life than that claimed. Use a 5% significance level.

9 A fertiliser manufacturer claims that by using brand F fertiliser the yield of fruit bushes will be increased. A random sample of 14 fruit bushes is fertilised with brand F and the resulting yields, x, are summarised by $\sum x = 90.8$, $\sum x^2 = 600$. The yield of bushes fertilised using the usual fertiliser is normally distributed with a mean of 6 kg per bush.
Test, at the 2.5% significance level, the manufacturer's claim.

10 A nuclear reprocessing company claims that the amount of radiation within a reprocessing building in which there had been an accident has been reduced to an acceptable level by their clean-up team. The amount of radiation x at 20 sites within the building, in suitable units, is summarised by $\sum x = 21.7$, $\sum x^2 = 28.4$. Before the accident the acceptable level of radiation in the building was normally distributed with a mean of 1.00. Test, at the 0.10 level, whether or not the claim is justified.

2.3 Confidence interval for the mean of a normal distribution with unknown variance

If a random sample $X_1, X_2, \ldots, X_n$ is selected from $N(\mu, \sigma^2)$ then you can obtain an estimate for the mean μ of the distribution by using $\dfrac{\sum X}{n} = \overline{X}$ as an estimator. You have seen that this is an unbiased estimator, but as in Statistics 3 it would be more helpful if you could give a range of values of μ such that μ will be captured within that range on, for example, 95% of the occasions on which a sample is taken. This is the 95% confidence interval of Statistics 3.

If the variance σ^2 of the population is unknown, S^2 can be used as an estimator for σ^2, and you know that $t = \dfrac{(\overline{X} - \mu)}{\dfrac{S}{\sqrt{n}}}$ has a t_{n-1}-distribution. Using the t-distribution table it is possible, given a value of n, to find a value of t such that $P\left(\dfrac{(\overline{X} - \mu)}{\dfrac{S}{\sqrt{n}}} > t \right) = 0.025$

and $\text{P}\left(\dfrac{(\bar{X}-\mu)}{\dfrac{S}{\sqrt{n}}}<-t\right)=0.025$. We can call these values the

t_{n-1} values for 0.025 probability (written $t_{(n-1)}(0.025)$ for short). Thus

$$\text{P}\left(-t_{(n-1)}(0.025)<\dfrac{(\bar{X}-\mu)}{\dfrac{S}{\sqrt{n}}}<t_{(n-1)}(0.025)\right)=0.95$$

Look at the inequality inside the brackets and try to isolate μ:

$$-t_{(n-1)}(0.025)\times\dfrac{S}{\sqrt{n}}<\bar{X}-\mu<t_{(n-1)}(0.025)\times\dfrac{S}{\sqrt{n}}$$

$$-t_{(n-1)}(0.025)\times\dfrac{S}{\sqrt{n}}-\bar{X}<-\mu<t_{(n-1)}(0.025)\times\dfrac{S}{\sqrt{n}}-\bar{X}$$

Multiplying by -1 and altering the inequality gives

$$\bar{X}-t_{(n-1)}(0.025)\times\dfrac{S}{\sqrt{n}}<\mu<\bar{X}+t_{(n-1)}(0.025)\times\dfrac{S}{\sqrt{n}}$$

If you have a specific estimate $\bar{x}$, and an associated estimate s, this becomes

$$\bar{x}-t_{(n-1)}(0.025)\times\dfrac{s}{\sqrt{n}}<\mu<\bar{x}+t_{(n-1)}(0.025)\times\dfrac{s}{\sqrt{n}}$$

The upper and lower values are again called the confidence limits.

Thus the 95% confidence limits are given by $\bar{x}\pm t_{(n-1)}(0.025)\times\dfrac{s}{\sqrt{n}}$.

The 95% confidence interval for the mean of a normal distribution with unknown variance is given by

$$\left(\bar{x}-t_{(n-1)}(0.025)\times\dfrac{s}{\sqrt{n}},\ \bar{x}+t_{(n-1)}(0.025)\times\dfrac{s}{\sqrt{n}}\right)$$

In the same way, the 90% confidence limits are given by

$$\bar{x}\pm t_{(n-1)}(0.05)\times\dfrac{s}{\sqrt{n}}$$

The 90% confidence interval for the mean of a normal distribution with unknown variance is given by

$$\left(\bar{x}-t_{(n-1)}(0.05)\times\dfrac{s}{\sqrt{n}},\ \bar{x}-t_{(n-1)}(0.05)\times\dfrac{s}{\sqrt{n}}\right)$$

In general

■ The $100(1 - \alpha)\%$ confidence limits are given by

$$\bar{x} \pm t_{(n-1)}\left(\tfrac{\alpha}{2}\right) \times \frac{s}{\sqrt{n}}$$

■ The $100(1 - \alpha)\%$ confidence interval for the mean of a normal distribution with unknown variance is given by

$$\left(\bar{x} - t_{(n-1)}\left(\tfrac{\alpha}{2}\right) \times \tfrac{s}{\sqrt{n}}, \; \bar{x} + t_{(n-1)}\left(\tfrac{\alpha}{2}\right) \times \frac{s}{\sqrt{n}} \right)$$

Example 5

A sample of 6 trout taken from a river had their lengths (in centimetres) measured. The lengths of the fish were as follows:

$$26.8 \quad 26.0 \quad 25.8 \quad 25.5 \quad 24.3 \quad 24.6$$

Assuming that the lengths of trout are normally distributed, find a 90% confidence interval for the mean length of trout in the river.

Using a calculator gives $\bar{x} = 25.5$ and $s^2 = 0.8560$.

$$s = \sqrt{0.8560} = 0.9252$$

The 90% confidence limits for $\bar{x}$ are

$$\bar{x} \pm t_5(5\%)\frac{s}{\sqrt{n}} = 25.5 \pm 2.015 \times \frac{0.9252}{\sqrt{6}}$$

$$= 25.5 \pm 0.761$$

The 90% confidence interval is (24.739, 26.261).

Example 6

The percentage starch content of potatoes is normally distributed with mean μ. In order to assess the mean value of the starch content a random sample of twelve potatoes is selected and their starch content measured. The percentages of starch contents obtained were as follows:

$$23.2 \quad 20.3 \quad 18.6 \quad 20.0 \quad 20.8 \quad 21.6 \quad 19.4 \quad 18.7 \quad 22.1 \quad 19.5 \quad 21.3 \quad 22.6$$

Find a 95% confidence interval for the mean.

Using a calculator, $\bar{x} = 20.675$ and $s = 1.513$.

The 95% confidence limits for $\bar{x}$ are

$$\bar{x} \pm t_{11}(2.5\%)\frac{s}{\sqrt{n}} = 20.675 \pm 2.201 \times \frac{1.513}{\sqrt{12}}$$

$$= 20.675 \pm 0.961$$

The 95% confidence interval is (19.714, 21.636).

2.4 Selecting the right test and confidence interval for a mean

You have seen that there are several different tests of means and different methods of calculating confidence intervals. The test selected depends on whether or not the variance of the population is known, and whether or not the sample size is large. You may perhaps be a little confused about when each is used. You could be tested in the examination on the work done in Statistics 3, so you should be aware of when each test or confidence interval is used. The following table should help you.

Variance	Sample size	Test statistic	95% confidence limits	90% confidence limits
σ^2 known	Large or small	$\dfrac{\overline{X} - \mu}{\dfrac{\sigma}{\sqrt{n}}} \sim N(0, 1)$	$\bar{x} \pm 1.96 \times \dfrac{\sigma}{\sqrt{n}}$	$\bar{x} \pm 1.6449 \times \dfrac{\sigma}{\sqrt{n}}$
σ^2 unknown	Large	$\dfrac{\overline{X} - \mu}{\dfrac{S}{\sqrt{n}}} \approx N(0, 1)$	$\bar{x} \pm 1.96 \times \dfrac{s}{\sqrt{n}}$	$\bar{x} \pm 1.6449 \times \dfrac{s}{\sqrt{n}}$
σ^2 unknown	Small	$\dfrac{\overline{X} - \mu}{\dfrac{S}{\sqrt{n}}} \sim t_{n-1}$	$\bar{x} \pm t_{n-1}(2.5\%) \times \dfrac{s}{\sqrt{n}}$	$\bar{x} \pm t_{n-1}(5\%) \times \dfrac{s}{\sqrt{n}}$

Exercise 2B

1 A test on the life (in hours) of a certain make of torch batteries gave the following results:

> 20.3 17.3 25.0 18.4 16.3 24.8 24.3 21.2

Assuming that the lifetime of batteries is normally distributed, find a 90% confidence interval for the mean.

2 A sample of size 16 taken from a normal population with unknown variance gave the following sample values: $\bar{x} = 12.4$, $s^2 = 21.0$. Find a 95% confidence interval for the population mean.

3 The mean heights (measured in centimetres) of six male students at a college were as follows:

> 182 178 183 180 169 184

Calculate

(a) a 90% confidence interval, and

(b) a 95% confidence interval for the mean height of male students at the college. You may assume that the heights are normally distributed.

4 The masses (in grams) of 10 nails selected at random from a bin of 90 cm long nails were

$$9.7 \quad 10.2 \quad 11.2 \quad 9.4 \quad 11.0 \quad 11.2 \quad 9.8 \quad 9.8 \quad 10.0 \quad 11.3$$

Calculate a 98% confidence interval for the mean mass of nails, assuming that their mass is normally distributed.

5 It is known that the length of men's feet is normally distributed. A random sample of the feet of 8 adult males gave the following readings of length (in cm):

$$28.4 \quad 21.8 \quad 27.2 \quad 30.1 \quad 29.7 \quad 27.8 \quad 27.5 \quad 31.6$$

Calculate a 99% confidence interval for the mean lengths of men's feet based upon these results.

6 A random sample of 26 students from the sixth form of a school sat an intelligence test that measured their IQs. The results are summarised below:

$$\bar{x} = 122 \quad s^2 = 225$$

Assuming that the IQ is normally distributed, calculate a 95% confidence interval for the mean IQ of the students.

2.5 The distribution of the variance of a sample taken from a normal distribution

If you take a sample of n independent observations $X_1, X_2, \ldots, X_n$ with sample mean $\bar{X}$ then $S^2 = \dfrac{1}{n-1} \sum (X_i - \bar{X})^2$ is an unbiased estimator of σ^2.

Different samples from the same population will give different estimates for μ and σ^2, so in the same way that $\bar{x}$ is a particular value of the random variable $\bar{X}$, s^2 is a particular value of a random variable S^2.

If the population is normal with mean μ and variance σ^2 then $Z = \dfrac{(\overline{X} - \mu)}{\dfrac{\sigma}{\sqrt{n}}}$ has a $N(0, 1)$ distribution, but what about the distribution of S^2?

The distribution of S^2 is not easy to find, and is beyond the scope of this book, but the distribution of $\dfrac{(n-1)S^2}{\sigma^2}$ is known, and is a distribution you met in Statistics 3, namely the chi-squared distribution with $n - 1$ degrees of freedom.

■ $\dfrac{(n-1)S^2}{\sigma^2} \sim \chi^2_{(n-1)}$

Percentage points of the chi-squared distribution

As before, percentage points for the $\chi^2_{(n-1)}$-distribution are given in the Appendix, Table 5. The number of degrees of freedom $v = n - 1$ are given down the left-hand side of the table and the percentages along the top. To read the value of χ^2_v which is exceeded with probability p, you find the intersection of the p column with the v row.

For example, if you wish to find $\chi^2_{10}(0.05)$ you look down the 0.05 column until you meet the row $v = 10$, and read off 18.307. Because the χ^2-distribution is non-symmetric, both tails of the distribution are given in the table. For example, $\chi^2_{10}(0.95) = 3.940$ so the probability of χ^2_{10} exceeding 3.940 is 95%. You should note that the probability that χ^2_{10} is less than 3.940 is $100 - 95 = 5\%$.

2.6 Hypothesis test for the variance of a normal distribution

Suppose that a manufacturer of pistons for cars had a machine that finished the diameter of the piston to size. The machine was set up so that it produced the pistons with a diameter that was normally distributed with mean 60 mm and standard deviation 0.03 mm. After the machine had been running for some time a random sample of 15 was taken, and the mean of the sample was still 60 mm but the best estimate of the variance calculated from the sample was $0.002 \, \text{mm}^2$. The question the manufacturer wished to have answered is 'has the variance increased?'

As usual with such questions a significance level has to be set, so let us imagine that it is 5%.

Putting the manufacturer's question in the form of hypotheses, you get

$$H_0 : \sigma^2 = 0.03^2 \quad H_1 : \sigma^2 > 0.03^2$$

If H_0 is assumed true then $\dfrac{(n-1)S^2}{\sigma^2}$ will be a single observation from a χ^2 distribution.

Since in this case $s^2 > \sigma^2$ then, as in previous hypothesis tests, you would have to ask 'could you get the calculated value of $\dfrac{(n-1)s^2}{\sigma^2}$ if H_0 were true?' The critical value separating the acceptance and rejection regions will be the relevant percentage point of the χ_{n-1}^2-distribution.

In this case $v = n - 1 = 15 - 1 = 14$, and the percentage is 0.05.

From the table $\chi_{14}^2(0.05) = 23.685$, and the critical region is $\dfrac{(n-1)s^2}{\sigma^2} \geqslant 23.685$.

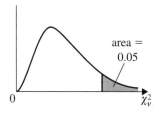

The value of the test statistic will be $\dfrac{(n-1)s^2}{\sigma^2}$.

In the manufacturer's case $\dfrac{(n-1)s^2}{\sigma^2} = \dfrac{(15-1)0.002}{0.03^2} = 31.11$.

31.11 is in the critical region so the result is significant and H_0 is rejected. The variance has increased.

Note that again there are 7 steps to be followed.

1. Write down the null hypothesis (H_0).
2. Write down the alternative hypothesis (H_1).
3. Specify α.
4. Write down the degrees of freedom v.
5. Write down the critical region.
6. Identify the population variance σ^2 and the unbiased estimate s^2 and calculate the value of the test statistic $\dfrac{(n-1)s^2}{\sigma^2}$.
7. Complete your test and state your conclusions. The following points should be addressed:
   (a) is the result significant?
   (b) what are the implications in the context of the original problem?

Example 7

A random sample of 12 observations is taken from a normal distribution with a variance of σ^2. The unbiased estimate of the population variance is calculated as 0.015.

Test, at the 5% level, the hypothesis that $\sigma^2 = 0.025$ against the alternative hypothesis that $\sigma^2 \neq 0.025$.

$H_0 : \sigma^2 = 0.025$

$H_1 : \sigma^2 \neq 0.025$.

$v = 11$.

This test is two-tailed so there will be 2 critical values.

From the table, $\chi^2_{11}(0.025) = 21.920$, $\chi^2_{11}(0.975) = 3.816$.

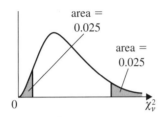

The critical region is $\dfrac{(n-1)s^2}{\sigma^2} \geqslant 21.920$ and $\dfrac{(n-1)s^2}{\sigma^2} \leqslant 3.816$.

$\sigma^2 = 0.025$,

$$s^2 = 0.015.$$

Test statistic

$$\frac{(n-1)s^2}{\sigma^2} = \frac{(12-1)0.015}{0.025}$$

$$= 6.6.$$

6.6 is not in the critical region so there is insufficient evidence for rejecting H_0. There has been no change in the variance.

Exercise 2C

1 Twenty random observations (x) are taken from a normal distribution with variance σ^2. The results are summarised as follows:

$$\sum x = 332.1, \ \sum x^2 = 5583.63$$

(a) Calculate an unbiased estimate for the population variance.

(b) Test, at the 5% significance level, the hypothesis
$H_0 : \sigma^2 = 1.5$ against the hypothesis $H_1 : \sigma^2 > 1.5$.

2 A random sample of 10 observations is taken from a normal distribution with variance σ^2 which is thought to be equal to 0.09. The results were as follows:

0.35, 0.42, 0.30, 0.26, 0.31, 0.30, 0.40, 0.33, 0.30, 0.40

Test, at the 0.025% level of significance, the hypothesis $H_0 : \sigma^2 = 0.09$ against the hypothesis $H_1 : \sigma^2 < 0.09$.

3 The following random observations are taken from a normal distribution which is thought to have a variance of 4.1:

2.1, 2.3, 3.5, 4.6, 5.0, 6.4, 7.1, 8.6, 8.7, 9.1

Test, at the 5% significance level, the hypothesis $H_0 : \sigma^2 = 4.1$ against the hypothesis $H_1 : \sigma^2 \neq 4.1$.

4 It is claimed that the masses of a particular component produced in a small factory have a mean mass of 10 g and a standard deviation of 1.12 g.

A random sample of 20 such components was found to have a variance of 1.15 g.

Test, at the 5% significance level, the hypothesis $H_0 : \sigma^2 = 1.12^2$ against the hypothesis $H_1 : \sigma^2 \neq 1.12^2$.

5 Rollers for use in roller bearings are produced on a certain machine. The rollers are supposed to have a mean diameter (μ) of 10 mm with a variance (σ^2) of 0.04 mm^2.

A random sample of 15 rollers from the machine have their diameters, x in mm, measured. The results are summarised below:

$$\sum x = 149.941, \sum x^2 = 1498.83$$

(a) Calculate unbiased estimates for μ and σ^2.

(b) Test, at the 5% significance level,

(i)   the hypothesis $\mu = 10$ against the hypothesis $\mu \neq 10$, using your estimate for σ^2 as the true variance of the population,

(ii) the hypothesis $\sigma^2 = 0.04$ against the hypothesis $\sigma^2 \neq 0.04$.

6 The diameters of the eggs of the little gull are approximately normally distributed with mean 4.11 cm and a variance of 0.19 cm^2.

A sample of 8 little gull eggs from a particular island which were measured had diameters in cm as follows:

4.4, 4.5, 4.1, 3.9, 4.4, 4.6, 4.5, 4.1

(a) Calculate an unbiased estimate for the variance of the population of little gulls on the island.

(b) Calculate the unbiased estimate of the mean diameter of the eggs and, test, at the 5% level, the hypothesis $\mu = 4.11$ against the hypothesis $\mu > 4.11$.

(c) Test, at the 10% significance level, the hypothesis $\sigma^2 = 0.19$ against the hypothesis $\sigma^2 \neq 0.19$.

7 Climbing rope produced by a certain manufacturer is known to have a mean tensile breaking strength (μ) of 170.2 kg and standard deviation 10.5 kg.

A new component is added to the material which will, it is claimed, decrease the standard deviation without altering the tensile strength. A random sample of 20 pieces of the new rope are tested to destruction and the tensile strength of each piece is noted. The results are used to calculate unbiased estimates of the mean strength and standard deviation of the population of new rope. These were found to be 172.4 kg and 8.5 kg.

(a) Test, at the 5% level, whether or not the variance has been reduced.

(b) What recommendation would you make to the manufacturer?

2.7 Confidence interval for the variance of a normal distribution

If a random sample $X_1, X_2, \ldots, X_n$ is taken from a $N(\mu, \sigma^2)$ population then $\dfrac{(n-1)S^2}{\sigma^2}$ has a χ^2_{n-1}-distribution. Using the table of percentage points of the distribution χ^2_{n-1} you can find given values of $\dfrac{(n-1)S^2}{\sigma^2}$ such that σ^2 will be captured within the interval between them on 95% of such occasions. Thus, assuming that the two tails are of equal size,

$$\chi^2_{n-1}(0.975) < \frac{(n-1)S^2}{\sigma^2} < \chi^2_{n-1}(0.025)$$

Turning the fractions upside down and reversing the inequality gives

$$\frac{1}{\chi^2_{n-1}(0.025)} < \frac{\sigma^2}{(n-1)S^2} < \frac{1}{\chi^2_{n-1}(0.975)}$$

and multiplying by $(n - 1)S^2$ gives

$$\frac{(n - 1)S^2}{\chi^2_{n-1}(0.025)} < \sigma^2 < \frac{(n - 1)S^2}{\chi^2_{n-1}(0.975)}$$

If you have a specific estimate s^2 this becomes

$$\frac{(n - 1)s^2}{\chi^2_{n-1}(0.025)} < \sigma^2 < \frac{(n - 1)s^2}{\chi^2_{n-1}(0.975)}$$

The values $\dfrac{(n - 1)s^2}{\chi^2_{n-1}(0.025)}$ and $\dfrac{(n - 1)s^2}{\chi^2_{n-1}(0.975)}$ are known as the lower and upper 95% confidence limits respectively, and the interval in between is called the 95% confidence interval.

The 95% confidence limits are $\dfrac{(n - 1)s^2}{\chi^2_{n-1}(0.025)}$ and $\dfrac{(n - 1)s^2}{\chi^2_{n-1}(0.975)}$.

The 95% confidence interval for the variance of a normal distribution is $\left\{ \dfrac{(n - 1)s^2}{\chi^2_{n-1}(0.025)}, \dfrac{(n - 1)s^2}{\chi^2_{n-1}(0.975)} \right\}$.

In a similar way:

The 90% confidence limits are $\dfrac{(n - 1)s^2}{\chi^2_{n-1}(0.05)}$ and $\dfrac{(n - 1)s^2}{\chi^2_{n-1}(0.95)}$.

The 90% confidence interval for the variance of a normal distribution is $\left\{ \dfrac{(n - 1)s^2}{\chi^2_{n-1}(0.05)}, \dfrac{(n - 1)s^2}{\chi^2_{n-1}(0.95)} \right\}$.

- **The $100(1 - \alpha)$% confidence limits are**

$$\frac{(n - 1)s^2}{\chi^2_{n-1}(\frac{\alpha}{2})} \text{ and } \frac{(n - 1)s^2}{\chi^2_{n-1}(1 - \frac{\alpha}{2})}$$

- **The $100(1 - \alpha)$% confidence interval for the variance of a normal**

  distribution is $\left\{ \dfrac{(n - 1)s^2}{\chi^2_{n-1}(1 - \frac{\alpha}{2})}, \dfrac{(n - 1)s^2}{\chi^2_{n-1}(1 - \frac{\alpha}{2})} \right\}$.

Example 8

In order to discover the accuracy of a new rifle, 8 marksmen were selected at random to fire the rifle at a target. The distances x, in mm, of the 8 shots from the centre of the target were as follows:

$$10, \ 14, \ 12, \ 8, \ 6, \ 11, \ 18, \ 14$$

Assuming that the distances are normally distributed, find 95% confidence limits for the variance.

Using a calculator gives $\bar{x} = 11.625$, $s^2 = 14.2679$.

First you find the percentage points of χ_7^2 from the table.

$$\chi_7^2(0.975) = 1.690 \quad \chi_7^2(0.025) = 16.013$$

Now find the critical points for the variance.

$$\frac{(n-1)s^2}{\chi_{n-1}^2(0.025)} = \frac{7 \times 14.2679}{16.013} = 6.2371$$

$$\frac{(n-1)s^2}{\chi_{n-1}^2(0.975)} = \frac{7 \times 14.2679}{1.690} = 59.0978$$

The 95% confidence interval for the variance is (6.24, 59.10).

Example 9

A company manufactures 12 amp electrical fuses.
A random sample of 10 fuses was taken from a batch and the failure current (x) measured for each. The results are summarised below:

$$\sum x = 118.9 \quad \sum x^2 = 1414.89$$

Assume that the data can be regarded as a random sample from a normal population.
(a) Calculate an unbiased estimate for the variance of the batch based upon the sample.
(b) Use your estimate from (a) to calculate a 95% confidence interval for
(i) the mean,
(ii) the standard deviation.

(a)
$$s^2 = \frac{1}{n-1} \left\{ \sum x^2 - \frac{(\sum x)^2}{n} \right\}$$

$$= \frac{1}{9} \left\{ 1414.89 - \frac{(118.9)^2}{10} \right\}$$

$$= 0.1299$$

(b) (i)
$$\bar{x} = \frac{\sum x}{n}$$

$$= \frac{118.9}{10}$$

$$= 11.89$$

The 95% confidence limits for the mean are given by

$$\bar{x} \pm t_9(0.025) \frac{\sigma}{\sqrt{n}}$$

$$= 11.89 \pm 2.262 \sqrt{\frac{0.1299}{10}}$$

$$= 11.89 \pm 0.2578$$

The 95% confidence interval is (11.632, 12.148).

(ii) The percentage points are

$$\chi_9^2(0.975) = 2.700 \text{ and } \chi_9^2(0.025) = 19.023$$

The critical points are

$$\frac{(n-1)s^2}{\chi_{n-1}^2(0.975)} = \frac{9 \times 0.1299}{2.7} = 0.4330$$

$$\frac{(n-1)s^2}{\chi_{n-1}^2(0.025)} = \frac{9 \times 0.1299}{19.023} = 0.0615$$

The 95% confidence interval for the variance is (0.0615, 0.4330).

Exercise 2D

1 A random sample of 15 observations of a normal population gave an unbiased estimate for the variance of the population of $s^2 = 4.8$. Calculate a 95% confidence interval for the population variance.

2 A random sample of 20 observations of a normally distributed variable X is summarised by $\sum x = 132.4$ and $\sum x^2 = 884.3$. Calculate a 90% confidence interval for the variance of X.

3 A random sample of 14 observations was taken from a population that is assumed to be normally distributed. The resulting values were

2.3, 3.9, 3.5, 2.2, 2.6, 2.5, 2.3, 3.9, 2.1, 3.6, 2.1, 2.7, 3.2, 3.4

Calculate a 95% confidence interval for the population variance.

4   A random sample of female voles were trapped in a wood.
Their lengths (in cm, excluding tails) were 7.5, 8.4, 10.1, 6.2,
and 8.4.
Assuming that this is a sample from a normal distribution,
calculate 95% confidence intervals for:
(a) the mean length,
(b) the variance of the lengths of female voles.

5   (a) A random sample of 10 is taken from the annual rainfall
figures, x cm, in a certain district. The result is summarised by
$\sum x = 621$ and $\sum x^2 = 38\,938$.
Calculate 90% confidence limits for
(i)   the mean annual rainfall,
(ii) the variance of the annual rainfall.
(b) What assumption have you made in part (a)?

6   A new variety of small daffodil is grown in the trial ground of
a nursery. During the flowering period a random sample of
10 flowers was taken and the lengths of their stalks were
measured. The results were as follows:

   266, 254, 215, 220, 253, 230, 216, 248, 234, 244 mm

Assuming that the lengths are normally distributed, calculate
95% confidence intervals for the mean and variance of the
lengths.

SUMMARY OF KEY POINTS

1   If a random sample of n observations $X_1, X_2, \ldots, X_n$ is
selected from $N(\mu, \sigma^2)$ then

$$\frac{(\bar{X} - \mu)}{\frac{S}{\sqrt{n}}} \sim t_{n-1}$$

2   The $100(1 - \alpha)\%$ confidence interval for the mean μ of a
normal distribution is

$$\left\{ \bar{x} - t_{n-1}\left(\tfrac{\alpha}{2}\right) \times \frac{s}{\sqrt{n}},\ \bar{x} + t_{n-1}\left(\tfrac{\alpha}{2}\right) \times \frac{s}{\sqrt{n}} \right\}$$

3 If a random sample of n observations $X_1, X_2, \ldots, X_n$ is selected from $N(\mu, \sigma^2)$ then

$$\frac{(n-1)S^2}{\sigma^2} \sim \chi^2_{n-1}$$

4 The $100(1-\alpha)\%$ confidence interval for the variance of a normal distribution is

$$\left\{ \frac{(n-1)s^2}{\chi^2_{n-1}\left(\frac{\alpha}{2}\right)}, \frac{(n-1)s^2}{\chi^2_{n-1}\left(1-\frac{\alpha}{2}\right)} \right\}$$

Review exercise 1

1 The random variable X is binomially distributed. A sample of 15 observations is taken and it is desired to test $H_0 : p = 0.35$ against $H_1 : p > 0.35$ using a 5% significance level.
(a) Find the critical region for this test.
(b) State the probability of making a type I error for this test.
The true value of p was found later to be 0.5.
(c) Calculate the power of this test.

2 The random variable X has a Poisson distribution. A sample is taken and it is desired to test $H_0 : \lambda = 3.5$ against $H_1 : \lambda < 3.5$ using a 5% significance level.
(a) Find the critical region for this test.
(b) State the probability of committing a type I error.
Given that the true value of λ is 3.0,
(c) find the power of this test.

3 The random variable $X \sim N(\mu, 9)$. A random sample of 18 observations of X is taken, and it is desired to test $H_0 : \mu = 8$ against $H_1 : \mu \neq 8$, at the 5% significance level. The test statistic to be used is $Z = \dfrac{\bar{X} - \mu}{\dfrac{\sigma}{\sqrt{n}}}$.

(a) Find the critical region for this test.
(b) State the probability of a type I error.
Given that μ was later found to be 7,
(c) find the probability of making a type II error.
(d) State the power of this test.

4 A single observation, x, is taken from a Poisson distribution with parameter λ. The observation is used to test $H_0 : \lambda = 4.5$ against $H_1 : \lambda > 4.5$. The critical region chosen for this test was $x \geqslant 8$.

(a) Find the size of this test.

(b) The table below gives the power of the test for different values of λ.

λ	1	2	3	4	5	6	7	8	9	10
Power	0	0.0011	0.0019	r	0.01340	s	0.4013	0.5470	t	0.7798

(i) Find values for r, s and t.

(ii) Using graph paper plot the power function against λ.

5 In a binomial experiment consisting of 15 trials, X represents the number of successes and p the probability of success. In a test of $H_0 : p = 0.45$ against $H_1 : p < 0.45$ the critical region for the test was $X \leqslant 3$.

(a) Find the size of the test.

(b) Use the table of the binomial cumulative distribution function to complete the table given below.

p	0.1	0.2	0.3	0.4	0.5
Power	0.944	s	0.2969	t	0.0176

(c) Draw the graph of the power function for this test.

6 A bag contains 25 balls of which an unknown number, m, are coloured red ($3 < m \leqslant 22$). Two of the balls are drawn from the bag and the number of red balls, X, is noted. It is desired to estimate m by $\hat{m} = cX$.

(a) Calculate a value for c if the estimate is to be unbiased.

The balls are replaced and a second draw of 3 balls is made and the number of red balls, Y, is noted.

(b) Calculate $E(Y)$.

(c) Show that $Z = \dfrac{25}{2}\left(\dfrac{X}{2} + \dfrac{Y}{3}\right)$ is an unbiased estimator of m.

7 A bag contains 25 balls of which an unknown number, m, are green ($4 < m \leqslant 21$).

Three balls are drawn from the bag and the number, X, of green balls is recorded. The balls are replaced and four balls are drawn with the number, Y, of green balls noted.

Three estimators of p, the probability of getting a green ball, are proposed: (i) $\dfrac{X+Y}{7}$ (ii) $\dfrac{3X+4Y}{25}$ (iii) $\dfrac{4X+3Y}{24}$.

(a) Show that all three are unbiased estimators of p.

(b) Find which is the most efficient estimator.

8 A random sample of 14 observations is taken from a normal distribution. The sample has a mean $\bar{x} = 30.4$ and a sample variance $s^2 = 36$.

It is suggested that the population mean is 28. Test this hypothesis at the 5% level of significance.

9 A random sample of 8 observations is taken from a random variable X that is normally distributed. The sample gave the following summary statistics:

$$\sum x^2 = 970.25, \ \sum x = 85$$

The population mean is thought to be 10. Test this hypothesis against the alternative hypothesis that the mean is greater than 10.

10 Six eggs selected at random from the daily output of a battery of hens had the following weights in grams:

$$55, \quad 50, \quad 53, \quad 53, \quad 52, \quad 54$$

Calculate 95% confidence intervals for

(a) the mean,

(b) the variance of the population from which these eggs were taken.

11 A sample of size 18 was taken from a random variable X which was normally distributed, producing the following summary statistics:

$$\bar{x} = 9.8, \ s^2 = 0.49$$

Calculate 95% confidence intervals for

(a) the mean,

(b) the variance of the population.

12 A random sample of 14 observations was taken of a random variable X which was normally distributed. The sample had a mean $\bar{x} = 23.8$, and a variance $s^2 = 1.8$.

Calculate

(a) a 95% confidence interval for the variance of the population,

(b) a 90% confidence interval for the variance of the population.

13 In a binomial experiment consisting of 10 trials the random variable X represents the number of successes, and p is the probability of a success.

In a test of $H_0 : p \leqslant 0.3$ against $H_1 : p > 0.3$, a critical region of $x \geqslant 7$ is used.

Find the power of this test when

(a) $p = 0.4$,

(b) $p = 0.8$.

(c) Comment on your results. [E]

14 Explain briefly what you understand by

(a) a type I error.

(b) the size of the critical region of a significance test.

A single observation is made on a random variable X, where $X \sim N(\mu, 10)$. The observation, x, is to be used to test $H_0 : \mu = 20$ against $H_1 : \mu > 20$. The critical region is chosen to be $x \geqslant 25$.

(c) Find the size of the critical region. [E]

15 A company buys rope from Bindings Ltd and it is known that the number of faults per 100 m of their rope follows a Poisson distribution with mean 2. The company is offered 100 m of rope by Tiemeup, a newly established rope manufacturer. The company is concerned that the rope from Tiemeup might be of poor quality.

(a) Write down the null and alternative hypotheses appropriate for testing that rope from Tiemeup is in fact as reliable as that from Bindings Ltd.

(b) Derive a critical region to test your null hypothesis with a size of approximately 0.05.

(c) Calculate the power of this test if rope from Tiemeup contains an average of 4 faults per 100 m. [E]

16 A manufacturer claims that the lifetime of its batteries is normally distributed with mean 21.5 hours. A laboratory tests 8 batteries and find the lifetimes of these batteries to be as follows:

19.7   18.4   22.2   20.8   16.9   25.3   23.2   21.1

Stating clearly your hypotheses, examine whether or not these lifetimes indicate that the batteries have a shorter mean lifetime than that claimed by the company. Use a 5% level of significance. [E]

17 The number of faulty garments produced per day by
machinists in a clothing factory has a Poisson distribution
with mean 2. A new machinist is trained and the number of
faulty garments made in one day by the new machinist is
counted.

(a) Write down the appropriate null and alternative
hypotheses involved in testing the theory that the new
machinist is at least as reliable as the other machinists.

(b) Derive a critical region, of size approximately, 0.05, to test
the null hypothesis.

(c) Calculate the power of this test if the new machinist
produces an average of 3 faulty garments per day.

The number of faulty garments produced by the new
machinist over three randomly selected days is counted.

(d) Derive a critical region, of approximately the same size as
in part (b), to test the null hypothesis.

(e) Calculate the power of this test if the machinist produces
an average of 3 faulty garments per day.

(f) Comment briefly on the difference between the two tests.

[E]

18 A single observation, x, is to be taken from a Poisson
distribution with parameter μ.

This observation is to be used to test $H_0 : \mu \geqslant 6$ against
$H_1 : \mu < 6$. The critical region is chosen to be $x \leqslant 2$.

(a) Find the size of the critical region.

(b) Show that the power function for this test is given by
$\frac{1}{2} e^{-\mu}(2 + 2\mu + \mu^2)$.

The table below gives the values of the power function to
2 decimal places.

μ	1.0	1.5	2.0	4.0	5.0	6.0	7.0
Power	0.92	0.81	s	0.24	t	0.06	0.03

(c) Calculate the values of s and t.

(d) Draw a graph of the power function.

(e) Find the range of values of μ for which the power of this
test is greater than 0.8.

[E]

19 A diabetic patient monitors his blood glucose in mmol/l at random times of the day over several days. The following is a random sample of the results for this patient:

  5.1 5.8 6.1 6.8 6.2 5.1 6.3 6.6 6.1 7.9 5.8 6.5

Assuming the data to be normally distributed, calculate a 95% confidence interval for

(a) the mean of the population of blood glucose readings,

(b) the standard deviation of the population of blood glucose readings.

The level of blood glucose varies throughout the day according to the consumption of food and the amount of exercise taken during the day.

(c) Comment on the suitability of the patient's method of data collection.   [E]

20 The random variable X has the following distribution:

x	0	1
$P(X = x)$	q	p

(a) Find $E(X)$ and $Var(X)$.

A random sample X_1, X_2, X_3, is taken from the distribution in order to estimate p.

(b) Find the condition which must be satisfied by the constants a_1, a_2, a_3, if $a_1X_1 + a_2X_2 + a_3X_3$ is to be an unbiased estimator of p.

(c) Find the variance of this estimator.

The following estimators are proposed:

(i) $\frac{1}{6}X_1 + \frac{1}{3}X_2 + \frac{1}{2}X_3$

(ii) $\frac{1}{3}X_1 + \frac{1}{6}X_2 + \frac{5}{12}X_3$

(iii) $\frac{7}{12}X_1 + \frac{5}{12}X_2$

(d) Of these three estimators, find the best unbiased estimator.   [E]

21 Two sets of binomial trials were carried out and in both sets the probability of success is p. In the first set there were X successes out of n trials and in the second set there were Y successes out of m trials.

Possible estimators for p are $\hat{p}_1 = \frac{1}{2}\left(\frac{X}{n} + \frac{Y}{m}\right)$ and $\hat{p}_2 = \frac{X + Y}{n + m}$.

(a) Show that both $\hat{p}_1$ and $\hat{p}_2$ are unbiased estimators of p.

(b) Find the variances of $\hat{p}_1$ and $\hat{p}_2$.

(c) If $n = 10$ and $m = 20$ state, giving a reason, which estimator you would use. [E]

22 A woollen mill produces scarves. The mill has several machines, each operated by a different person. Jane has recently started working at the mill and the supervisor wishes to check the lengths of the scarves Jane is producing. A random sample of 20 scarves is taken and the length, x cm, of each scarf is recorded. The results are summarised as

$$\sum x = 1428, \quad \sum x^2 = 102\,286$$

Assuming that the lengths of scarves produced by any individual follow a normal distribution,

(a) calculate a 95% confidence interval for the variance, σ^2, of the lengths of scarves produced by Jane.

The mill's owners require that 90% of scarves should be within 10 cm of the mean length.

(b) Find the value of σ that would satisfy this condition.

(c) Explain whether or not the supervisor should be concerned about the scarves Jane is producing. [E]

23 In order to discover the possible error in using a stopwatch, a student started the watch and stopped it again as quickly as she could. The times taken in centiseconds for 6 such attempts are recorded below:

$$10, \quad 13, \quad 14, \quad 10, \quad 13, \quad 9$$

Assuming that the times are normally distributed, find 95% confidence limits for

(a) the mean,

(b) the variance. [E]

24 (In this question $\max(a, b) = $ the greater of the two values a and b.) A palaeontologist was attempting to estimate the length of time, τ, in years, during which a small herbivorous dinosaur existed on Earth. He believed from other evidence that the earliest existence of the animal had been at the start of the Jurassic period.

Two examples of the animal had been discovered in the fossil record, at times t_1 and t_2 after the start of the Jurassic period. His model assumed that these times were values of two independent random variables T_1 and T_2 each having a continuous uniform distribution on the interval $[0, \tau]$. He considered three estimators for τ.

$$\tau_1 = T_1 + T_2, \quad \tau_2 = \sqrt{3} \mid T_2 - T_1 \mid, \quad \tau_3 = 1.5 \max(T_1, T_2)$$

He used appropriate probability theory and calculated the results shown in the table.

Variable	Expectation	Variance
T_1	$\dfrac{\tau}{2}$	$\dfrac{\tau^2}{12}$
$\mid T_2 - T_1 \mid$	$\dfrac{\tau}{3}$	$\dfrac{\tau^2}{18}$
$\max(T_1, T_2)$	$\dfrac{2\tau}{3}$	$\dfrac{\tau^2}{18}$

Using these results
(a) determine the bias of each of his estimators,
(b) find the variance of each of his estimators.

Using your results from (a) and (b), state, giving a reason,
(c) which estimator is the best of the three,
(d) which estimator is the worst.   [E]

25 A manufacturer claims that the car batteries which it produces have a mean lifetime of 24 months, with a standard deviation of 4 months. A garage selling the batteries doubts this claim and suggests that both values are in fact higher.
The garage monitors the lifetimes of 10 randomly selected batteries and finds that they have a mean lifetime of 27.2 months and a standard deviation of 5.2 months.
Stating clearly your hypotheses and using a 5% level of significance, test the claim made by the manufacturer for
(a) the standard deviation,
(b) the mean.
(c) State an assumption which has to be made when carrying out these tests.   [E]

26 The distance to take-off from a standing start of an aircraft was measured on twenty occasions. The results are summarised in the following table.

Distance (m)	Frequency
700–	3
710–	5
720–	9
730–	2
740–750	1

Assuming that distance to take-off is normally distributed, find 95% confidence intervals for

(a) the mean,

(b) the standard deviation.

It has been hypothesised that the mean distance to take-off is 725 m.

(c) Comment on this hypothesis in the light of your interval from part (a). [E]

27 The maximum weight that 50 cm lengths of a certain make of string can hold before breaking (the breaking strain) has a normal distribution with mean 40 kg and standard deviation 5 kg. The manufacturer of the string has developed a new process which should increase the mean breaking strain of the string but should not alter the standard deviation. Ten randomly selected pieces of string are tested and their breaking strains, in kg, are

51, 48, 37, 46, 36, 53, 34, 49, 47, 50

(a) Stating your hypotheses clearly, test at the 5% level of significance whether or not the new process has altered the variance.

In the light of your conclusion to the test in part (a),
(b) test whether or not there is evidence that the new process has increased the mean breaking strain. State your hypotheses clearly and use a 5% level of significance.

(c) Explain briefly your choice of test in part (b). [E]

28 A certain gambler always calls heads when a coin is tossed. Before he uses a coin he tests it to see whether or not it is fair and uses the following hypotheses:

$$H_0 : p = \tfrac{1}{2} \quad H_1 : p < \tfrac{1}{2}$$

where p is the probability that the coin lands heads on a particular toss. Two tests are proposed.

In test A the coin is tossed 10 times and H_0 is rejected if the number of heads is 2 or fewer.

(a) Find the size of test A.

(b) Explain why the power of test A is given by

$$(1 - p)^{10} + 10p(1 - p)^9 + 45p^2(1 - p)^8$$

In test B the coin is first tossed 5 times. If no heads result H_0 is immediately rejected. Otherwise the coin is tossed a further 5 times and H_0 is rejected if no heads appear on this second occasion.

(c) Find the size of test B.

(d) Find an expression for the power of test B in terms of p.

The power for test A and the power for test B are given in the table for various values of p.

p	0.1	0.2	0.25	0.3	0.35	0.4
Power for test A	0.9298	0.6778		0.3828		0.1673
Power for test B	0.8323	0.5480	0.4183	0.3079	0.2186	0.1495

(e) Find the power for test A when p is 0.25 and 0.35.

(f) Giving a reason, advise the gambler which test he should use. [E]

29 A company knows from previous experience that the time taken by maintenance engineers to repair a particular electrical fault on a complex piece of electrical equipment is 3.5 hours on average with a standard deviation of 0.5 hours.

A new method of repair has been devised, but before converting to this new method the company takes a random sample of 10 of its engineers and each engineer carries out a repair using the new method. The time, x hours, it takes each of them to carry out the repair is recorded and the data are summarised below:

$$\sum x = 34.2 \quad \sum x^2 = 121.6$$

Assume that the data can be regarded as a random sample from a normal population.

(a) For the new repair method, calculate an unbiased estimate of the variance.

(b) Use your estimate from (a) to calculate for the new repair method a 95% confidence interval for

(i) the mean,

(ii) the standard deviation.

(c) Use your calculations and the given data to compare the two repair methods in order to advise the company as to which method to use.

(d) Suggest an alternative way of comparing the two methods of repair using the 10 randomly chosen engineers. [E]

30 It is believed that the random variable X, representing the length of time, in hours, that office workers can sit before incurring back pain, has a normal distribution. The times taken by a random sample of 30 office workers were recorded and summarised in the following statistics:

$$\sum x = 81.00, \quad \sum x^2 = 237.26$$

(a) Find a 95% confidence interval for the mean.

(b) Show that a 95% confidence interval for the variance is (0.41, 1.16).

A manufacturer of office furniture claims to have produced a new back support for office chairs that enables office workers to sit for longer periods without incurring back pain. A decision is made to test the new back support on a random sample of 10 office workers. The random variable Y represents the length of time, in hours, that office workers can sit using the new back support before incurring back pain. The distribution of Y is $N(\mu, 0.75^2)$.

(c) Find the critical region for Y to test $H_0 : \mu = 3$ against $H_1 : \mu > 3$, using a size of 5%.

The value of μ using the new back support is 3.5.

(d) Find the power of the test in part (c). [E]

Two-sample procedures

3

Chapter 2 was concerned with making deductions about populations by taking a single sample from a normal distribution; this chapter deals with the questions you can ask when two separate random samples are taken from normal distributions.

A condition required by the hypothesis tests that are done later in this chapter is that the two population variances be equal. For this reason a test to see if two independent random samples are from normal populations with equal variances is introduced early in the chapter. First we introduce a new distribution.

3.1 The *F*-distribution

Suppose that you take a random sample of n_x observations from a $N(\mu_x, \sigma_x^2)$ distribution and independently a random sample of n_y observations from a $N(\mu_y, \sigma_y^2)$ distribution. Unbiased estimators for the two population variances are S_x^2 and S_y^2.

In section 2.5 of chapter 2 you saw that

$$\frac{(n_x - 1)S_x^2}{\sigma_x^2} \sim \chi_{n_x - 1}^2 \text{ and } \frac{(n_y - 1)S_y^2}{\sigma_y^2} \sim \chi_{n_y - 1}^2$$

It follows from this that
$$\frac{\dfrac{(n_x - 1)S_x^2}{\sigma_x^2}}{\dfrac{(n_y - 1)S_y^2}{\sigma_y^2}} \sim \frac{\chi_{n_x - 1}^2}{\chi_{n_y - 1}^2}$$

so
$$\frac{S_x^2/\sigma_x^2}{S_y^2/\sigma_y^2} \sim \frac{(n_y - 1)\chi_{n_x - 1}^2}{(n_x - 1)\chi_{n_y - 1}^2} \text{ and } \frac{S_y^2/\sigma_y^2}{S_x^2/\sigma_x^2} \sim \frac{(n_x - 1)\chi_{n_y - 1}^2}{(n_y - 1)\chi_{n_x - 1}^2}$$

Distributions such as $\dfrac{(n_y - 1)\chi_{n_x - 1}^2}{(n_x - 1)\chi_{n_y - 1}^2}$ were first studied by Sir Ronald Fisher, and are named *F*-distributions in his honour.

The distribution $\dfrac{(n_y - 1)\chi_{n_x - 1}^2}{(n_x - 1)\chi_{n_y - 1}^2}$ has two parameters $(n_x - 1)$ and

$(n_y - 1)$ and is usually denoted by $F_{n_x - 1, n_y - 1}$, or by F_{v_1, v_2} where $v_1 = (n_x - 1)$ and $v_2 = (n_y - 1)$ i.e. if $n_x = 13$ and $n_y = 9$ the distribution would be an $F_{12, 8}$-distribution.

A typical distribution is shown below.

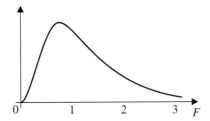

Since variances are always positive F is always greater than zero.

Now, if a sample of size n_x is taken from a normal random variable X and a sample of size n_y is taken from a normal random variable Y then

$$\frac{S_x^2/\sigma_x^2}{S_y^2/\sigma_y^2} \sim F_{n_x - 1, n_y - 1} \text{ and } \frac{S_y^2/\sigma_y^2}{S_x^2/\sigma_x^2} \sim F_{n_y - 1, n_x - 1}$$

Since $\dfrac{S_x^2/\sigma_x^2}{S_y^2/\sigma_y^2} \neq \dfrac{S_y^2/\sigma_y^2}{S_x^2/\sigma_x^2}$ it is clear that $F_{n_x - 1, n_y - 1} \neq F_{n_y - 1, n_x - 1}$.

Remember that the order is important. If S_x^2 is at the top of the fraction $\dfrac{S_x^2/\sigma_x^2}{S_y^2/\sigma_y^2}$, then $n_x - 1$ comes first after the F, but if S_y^2 is at the top then $n_y - 1$ comes first.

- **For a random sample of n_x observations from a $N(\mu_x, \sigma_x^2)$ distribution and an independent random sample of n_y observations from a $N(\mu_y, \sigma_y^2)$ distribution,**

$$\frac{S_x^2/\sigma_x^2}{S_y^2/\sigma_y^2} \sim F_{n_x - 1, n_y - 1}$$

3.2 *F*-distribution tables

The F-distribution has two parameters $v_1 = n_x - 1$ and $v_2 = n_y - 1$, and to get all distributions relating to all possible combinations of v_1 and v_2 would require very extensive tables. The numbers of degrees of freedom, v_1 and v_2, are used here because that is how they are described on the tables, but v_x and v_y could equally well be used.

The F-distribution is used mainly in hypothesis testing for variances, and so you are not really interested in all values of F_{v_1, v_2}.

The values of F_{v_1, v_2} that are of interest are the critical values, which are exceeded with probabilities of 5%, 1%, etc. These critical values are written F_{v_1, v_2} (0.05) or F_{v_1, v_2} (0.01). F_{v_1, v_2} (0.05) is illustrated below.

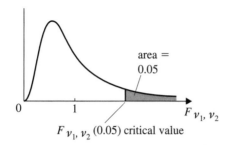

area = 0.05

0   1

F_{v_1, v_2}

F_{v_1, v_2} (0.05) critical value

A separate table is given for each significance level (Table 7 on page 125 in the Appendix is for the 1% (0.01) and 5% (0.05) significance levels). The first row at the top gives values of v_1 (remember that v_1 comes first after the F), and the first column on the left gives values of v_2. Where row and column meet gives the value of the critical point corresponding to the significance level of that table. A short extract from the 0.05 significance level table is given below.

Probability	v_2/v_1	1	2	3	4	5	6	8	10	12	24	∞
	1	161.4	199.5	215.7	224.6	230.2	234.0	238.9	241.9	243.9	249.1	254.3
0.05	2	18.51	19.00	19.16	19.25	19.30	19.33	19.37	19.40	19.41	19.46	19.50
	3	10.13	9.55	9.28	9.12	9.01	8.94	8.85	8.79	8.74	8.64	8.53
	4	7.71	6.94	6.59	6.39	6.26	6.16	6.04	5.96	5.91	5.77	5.63
	5	6.61	5.79	5.41	5.19	5.05	4.95	4.82	4.74	4.68	4.53	4.37
	6	5.99	5.14	4.76	4.53	4.39	4.28	4.15	4.06	4.00	3.84	3.67
	7	5.59	4.74	4.35	4.12	3.97	3.87	3.73	3.64	3.57	3.41	3.23
	8	5.32	4.46	4.07	3.84	3.69	3.58	3.44	3.35	3.28	3.12	2.93
	9	5.12	4.26	3.86	3.63	3.48	3.37	3.23	3.14	3.07	2.90	2.71

Example 1
Use the table to find
(a) $F_{5, 8}$ (0.05) critical point,
(b) $F_{8, 5}$ (0.05) critical point.

(a) Using the table, the critical point at the 5% level for $F_{5, 8}$ is at the intersection of the 5th column and the 8th row, and reads 3.69, so $F_{5, 8}$ (0.05) critical point = 3.69.
(b) The critical point of $F_{8, 5}$ is at the intersection of the 8th column and the 5th row and reads 4.82 so $F_{8, 5}$ (0.05) critical point = 4.82.

The 5% probability table enables you to read off for different values of v_1 and v_2 the value of F_{v_1, v_2} that is exceeded with probability 0.05 (the F_{v_1, v_2} (0.05) upper critical point).

The 1% probability table enables you to read off for different values of v_1 and v_2 the value of F_{v_1, v_2} that is exceeded with probability 0.01 (the F_{v_1, v_2} (0.01) upper critical point).

The table can also be used to find a value of F_{v_1, v_2} that is exceeded with probability 0.95 or, looking at it a different way, a value of F_{v_1, v_2} such that the probability of getting a lower value of F_{v_1, v_2} is 0.05 (the F_{v_1, v_2} (0.95) lower critical point). The region is shown below.

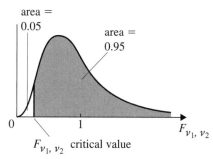

area = 0.05

area = 0.95

F_{v_1, v_2} critical value

It is done in the following way:

$$P(F_{v_1, v_2} < f) = P\left(\frac{\chi_{v_1}^2/v_1}{\chi_{v_2}^2/v_2} < f\right)$$

$$= P\left(\frac{1}{f} < \frac{\chi_{v_2}^2/v_2}{\chi_{v_1}^2/v_1}\right)$$

$$= P\left(\frac{1}{f} < F_{v_2, v_1}\right)$$

Notice that the degrees of freedom are interchanged when using a reciprocal to find the lower percentage point, and that for example

F_{v_1, v_2} (0.95) lower critical value $= \dfrac{1}{F_{v_2, v_1}(0.05) \text{ upper critical value}}$.

We usually use the following:

■ $F_{v_2, v_1} = \dfrac{1}{F_{v_1, v_2}}$

Example 2
Find critical values for
(a) $F_{8, 10}$ (0.95),
(b) $F_{10, 8}$ (0.95).

(a) $F_{8, 10}$ (0.95) critical value $= \dfrac{1}{F_{10, 8} (0.05) \text{ critical value}}$

$= \dfrac{1}{3.35}$

$= 0.2985$

$= 0.30$ (2 d.p.)

(b) $F_{10,8}(0.95)$ critical value $= \dfrac{1}{F_{8,10}(0.05) \text{ critical value}}$

$$= \dfrac{1}{3.07}$$
$$= 0.33 \text{ (2 d.p.)}$$

Example 3

Find the lower and upper 5% critical point for an $F_{a,b}$-distribution in each of the following cases:

(a) $a = 6, b = 10$,
(b) $a = 12, b = 8$.

(a) The upper critical value is $F_{6,10}(0.05) = 3.22$.

The lower 5% critical value is $F_{6,10}(0.95) = \dfrac{1}{F_{10,6}} = \dfrac{1}{4.06} = 0.25$.

(b) The upper critical value is $F_{12,8}(0.05) = 3.28$.

The lower 5% critical value is $F_{12,8}(0.95) = \dfrac{1}{F_{8,12}} = \dfrac{1}{2.85} = 0.35$.

Example 4

The random variable X follows an F-distribution with 8 and 10 degrees of freedom. Find $P\left(\dfrac{1}{5.81} < X < 5.06\right)$.

Looking at the upper tail $P(X > 5.06) = P(F_{8,10} > 5.06)$

From the tables $F_{8,10}(5\%) = 3.07$ and $F_{8,10}(1\%) = 5.06$.

So $P(X > 5.06) = 0.01$

and $P(X < 5.06) = 1 - 0.01 = 0.99$

Looking at the other tail $P\left(X < \dfrac{1}{5.81}\right) = P(F_{10,8} > 5.81)$

From the tables $F_{10,8}(5\%) = 3.35$ and $F_{10,8}(1\%) = 5.81$.

$\therefore$ $P\left(X < \dfrac{1}{5.81}\right) = 0.01$

Now $P\left(\dfrac{1}{5.81} < X < 5.06\right) = P(X > 5.06) - P\left(X < \dfrac{1}{5.81}\right)$

$$= 0.99 - 0.01$$
$$= 0.98$$

Example 5

The random variable X follows a $F_{6,12}$-distribution.

Find $P(X < 0.25)$.

$$P(X < 0.25) = P(F_{6,12} < 0.25) = P\left(F_{12,6} > \frac{1}{0.25}\right)$$
$$= P(F_{12,6} > 4)$$

From the tables $\qquad\qquad F_{12,6}(0.05) = 4$

$\therefore \qquad\qquad\qquad P(F_{12,6} > 4) = 0.05$

Exercise 3A

1 Find the upper 5% critical point for a $F_{a,b}$-distribution in each of the following cases:
   (a) $a = 12, b = 18,$
   (b) $a = 4, b = 11,$
   (c) $a = 6, b = 9.$

2 Find the lower 5% critical point for a $F_{a,b}$-distribution in each of the following cases:
   (a) $a = 6, b = 8,$
   (b) $a = 25, b = 12,$
   (c) $a = 5, b = 5.$

3 Find the upper 1% critical point for a $F_{a,b}$-distribution in each of the following cases:
   (a) $a = 12, b = 18,$
   (b) $a = 6, b = 16,$
   (c) $a = 5, b = 9.$

4 Find the lower 1% critical point for a $F_{a,b}$-distribution in each of the following cases:
   (a) $a = 3, b = 12,$
   (b) $a = 8, b = 12,$
   (c) $a = 5, b = 12.$

5 Find the lower and upper 5% critical point for a $F_{a,b}$-distribution in each of the following cases:
   (a) $a = 8, b = 10,$
   (b) $a = 12, b = 10,$
   (c) $a = 3, b = 5.$

6 The random variable X follows a $F_{40,12}$-distribution. Find $P(X < 0.5)$.

7 The random variable X follows a $F_{12,8}$-distribution.
   Find $P\left(\dfrac{1}{2.85} < X < 3.28\right).$

3.3 Hypothesis test that two independent random samples are from normal populations with equal variances

Customers in supermarkets expect the produce that they buy loose, e.g. potatoes, apples, etc., to be of a uniform size. When purchasing from suppliers, therefore, the managers of supermarkets are concerned not only with the mean size of the produce but also how variable that size is. Given two suppliers, the one selected is likely to be the one whose produce has the lowest variance. 'How,' you might ask, 'is the manager to tell if one variance is larger than the other, simply by taking a sample from each?' The following test is designed for such cases.

You begin by making the assumptions that the samples are drawn from normal populations. If you have two random samples of sizes n_x and n_y respectively then from section 3.1

$$\frac{S_x^2/\sigma_x^2}{S_y^2/\sigma_y^2} \sim F_{n_x-1,\,n_y-1}$$

If you assume that $\sigma_x^2 = \sigma_y^2$, then $\dfrac{\sigma_y^2}{\sigma_x^2} = 1$ and

$$\frac{S_x^2}{S_y^2} \sim F_{n_x-1,\,n_y-1}$$

■ **If a random sample of n_x observations is taken from a normal distribution with unknown variance σ^2 and an independent random sample of n_y observations is taken from a normal distribution with equal but unknown variance then**

$$\frac{S_x^2}{S_y^2} \sim F_{n_x-1,\,n_y-1}$$

If $\sigma_x^2 = \sigma_y^2$ then you would expect $\dfrac{S_x^2}{S_y^2}$ to be close to 1, but if $\sigma_x^2 > \sigma_y^2$ then you would expect it to be much greater than 1.

You wish to test the hypothesis $H_0 : \sigma_x^2 = \sigma_y^2$ against the alternative hypothesis $\sigma_x^2 > \sigma_y^2$. As when testing hypotheses before, if your value of $\dfrac{S_x^2}{S_y^2}$ is such that it could only occur under the null hypothesis with a probability $\leqslant \alpha$ (typically $\alpha = 0.05$) then you reject the null hypothesis; otherwise you have to conclude that there is insufficient evidence to reject the null hypothesis. The critical value $F_{v_x,\,v_y}(\alpha)$ can be read from the table.

Example 6

Two samples of size 13 and 9 are taken from normal distributions X and Y. The two samples give values $s_x^2 = 24$ and $s_y^2 = 18$. Test at the 5% level whether or not the variances of the populations from which the samples are drawn are the same by testing $H_0 : \sigma_x^2 = \sigma_y^2$ against the alternative hypothesis $H_1 : \sigma_x^2 > \sigma_y^2$.

The critical value is $F_{12,8}$ (5%) and, from the table, this is found to be 3.28.

The test statistic is $\dfrac{s_x^2}{s_y^2} = \dfrac{24}{18} = 1.33$ (notice that the larger variance is divided by the smaller).

$1.33 < 3.28$ so there is insufficient evidence to reject H_0; the two populations have equal variances.

In the above case the alternative hypothesis was $\sigma_x^2 > \sigma_y^2$. However, in other cases you may wish to test against the alternative hypothesis $\sigma_x^2 < \sigma_y^2$. In cases such as these, since the tables give only upper percentage values, the easiest thing to do is to put the larger estimated variance in the numerator, i.e. use $\dfrac{s_y^2}{s_x^2}$ so that you can then use the right-hand tail of F_{v_y, v_x}. This practice does not affect any other aspect of the test, but care must be taken to ensure that the degrees of freedom are used correctly and that the hypotheses are defined accurately.

Example 7

Two samples of size 7 and 11 are taken from normal distributions X and Y. The two samples give values $s_x^2 = 5$ and $s_y^2 = 25$. Test at the 5% level whether or not the variances of the populations from which the samples are drawn are the same by testing $H_0 : \sigma_x^2 = \sigma_y^2$ against the alternative hypothesis $H_1 : \sigma_x^2 < \sigma_y^2$. $\left(\text{Note} \right.$ the alternative hypothesis can be written $H_1 : \sigma_y^2 > \sigma_x^2$, so the test statistic becomes $\left. \dfrac{s_y^2}{s_x^2}.\right)$

The critical value is $F_{10,6}$ (5%) = 4.06.

The test statistic is $\dfrac{s_y^2}{s_x^2} = \dfrac{25}{5} = 5$.

$5 > 4.06$ so there is sufficient evidence to reject H_0. So $\sigma_x^2 < \sigma_y^2$.

There is of course the third type of alternative hypothesis. If you wish to test against the alternative hypothesis $\sigma_x^2 \neq \sigma_y^2$ you can take the larger value of s (s_l) and divide it by the smaller value (s_s)

so that the ratio $\dfrac{s_1^2}{s_s^2}$ will be >1, and since this is greater than 1 the left-hand tail can be ignored. The right-hand tail can be tested as before but you must remember that half the significance level α will be used at each tail, and the critical value will therefore be $F_{v_1, v_s}\left(\dfrac{\alpha}{2}\right)$.

Example 8

Two samples of size 11 and 13 are taken from normal distributions X and Y. The two samples give values $s_x^2 = 1.6$ and $s_y^2 = 2.4$. Test at the 10% level whether or not the variances of the populations from which the samples are drawn are equal by testing $H_0 : \sigma_x^2 = \sigma_y^2$ against the alternative hypothesis $H_1 : \sigma_x^2 \neq \sigma_y^2$.

Here Y has the larger variance so $v_1 = 13 - 1 = 12$, $v_s = 11 - 1 = 10$, $s_1^2 = 2.4$ and $s_s^2 = 1.6$.

The critical value is $F_{v_1, v_s}\left(\dfrac{\alpha}{2}\right) = F_{12, 10}(5\%) = 2.91$.

The test statistic is $\dfrac{s_1^2}{s_s^2} = \dfrac{2.4}{1.6} = 1.5$.

$1.5 < 2.91$, so there is insufficient evidence to reject H_0; the two variances are equal.

In all three of the above examples the larger variance was divided by the smaller variance and the critical value was found by using the F_{v_1, v_s}-distribution; the only difference was that when the test was two-tailed the significance level had to be half in each tail. This enables a simple set of rules to be used as follows.

1. Find s_1^2 and s_s^2, the larger and smaller variances respectively.
2. Write down the null hypothesis $H_0 : \sigma_1^2 = \sigma_s^2$.
3. Write down the alternative hypothesis $H_1 : \sigma_1^2 > \sigma_s^2$ (one-tailed), or $H_1 : \sigma_1^2 \neq \sigma_s^2$ (two-tailed).
4. Look up the critical value of F_{v_1, v_s}, where v_1 is the number of degrees of freedom of the distribution with the larger variance and v_s is the number of degrees of freedom of the distribution with the smaller variance. If a two-tailed test is used, α is halved (e.g. for a 10% significance level you would use $F_{v_1, v_s}(5\%)$ as the critical value.)
5. Write down the critical region.
6. Calculate $F_{\text{test}} = \dfrac{s_1^2}{s_s^2}$.
7. See whether F_{test} lies in the critical region or not and draw your conclusions. Relate these to the original problem.

Example 9

A manufacturer of wooden furniture stores some of its wood outside and some inside a special store. It is believed that the wood stored inside should have less variable hardness properties than that stored outside. A random sample of 25 pieces of wood stored outside was taken and compared with a random sample of 21 similar pieces taken from the inside store, with the following results:

	Outside	Inside
Sample size	25	21
Mean hardness (coded units)	110	122
Sum of squares about the mean	5190	3972

(a) Test at the 0.05 level whether or not the manufacturer's belief is correct.

(b) State any assumptions you have made in order to do this test.

(a)
$$s^2 = \frac{\sum (x_i - \bar{x})^2}{n - 1} \text{ so}$$

$$s^2_{\text{outside}} = \frac{5190}{24} = 216.25 \text{ and } s^2_{\text{inside}} = \frac{3972}{20} = 198.6$$

$$H_0 : \sigma_1^2 = \sigma_s^2, \quad H_1 : \sigma_1^2 > \sigma_s^2$$

Critical value $= F_{24, 20}(0.05) = 2.08$

$$F_{\text{test}} = \frac{216.25}{198.6} = 1.089$$

$1.089 < 2.08$, so there is insufficient evidence to reject H_0; wood stored inside is just as variable in hardness as wood stored outside.

(b) The assumption made is that the populations are normally distributed.

Exercise 3B

1 Random samples are taken from two normally distributed populations. There are 11 observations from the first population and the best estimate of the population variance is $s^2 = 7.6$. There are 7 observations from the second population and the best estimate of the population variance is $s^2 = 6.4$. Test at the 5% significance level the hypothesis $H_0 : \sigma_1^2 = \sigma_2^2$ against the alternative hypothesis $H_1 : \sigma_1^2 > \sigma_2^2$.

2 Random samples are taken from two normally distributed populations. There are 25 observations from the first population and the best estimate of the population variance is $s^2 = 0.42$. There are 41 observations from the second population and the best estimate of the population variance is $s^2 = 0.17$.

Test at the 1% significance level the hypothesis $H_0 : \sigma_1^2 = \sigma_2^2$ against the alternative hypothesis $H_1 : \sigma_1^2 > \sigma_2^2$.

3 Random samples are taken from two normally distributed populations. The summary statistics are given below.

Population	Sample size	$\sum x$	$\sum x^2$
1	9	355	36 369
2	6	158	16 375

Test, at the 10% significance level, whether or not the two distributions have equal variances.

4 Random samples are taken from two normally distributed populations. The size of the sample from the first population is $n_1 = 13$ and this gives an unbiased estimate of the population variance $s_1^2 = 36.4$. The figures for the second population are $n_2 = 9$ and $s_2^2 = 52.6$.

Test at the 5% significance level whether $\sigma_1^2 = \sigma_2^2$ or if $\sigma_2^2 > \sigma_1^2$.

5 Dining Chairs Ltd are in the process of selecting a make of glue for using on the joints of their furniture. There are two possible contenders – Goodstick, which is the more expensive, and Holdtight, the cheaper of the two.

The company are concerned that, while both glues are said to have the same adhesive power, one might be more variable than the other.

A series of trials are carried out with each glue and the joints tested to destruction. The force in newtons at which each joint fails is recorded. The results are as follows:

Goodstick 10.3   8.2   9.5   9.9   11.4
Holdtight   9.6   10.8   9.9   10.8   10.0   10.2

(a) Test at the 10% significance level whether or not the variances are equal.

(b) Which glue would you recommend and why?

6 Two different makes of handgun, A and B, have their sights adjusted by a marksman, and are then fired 6 times at separate, but identical, targets.

The distance, x mm, of each shot from the centre of the target was then measured. Summary results are given below:

	$\sum x$	$\sum x^2$
Gun A	11.8	248.6
Gun B	4.6	27.67

Assuming that the distances are normally distributed about the centre, test at the 2% significance level whether or not there is a difference in the variance of the distance from the centre of the target for these guns.

7 Bigborough council wishes to change the bulbs in their traffic lights at regular intervals so that there is very small probability that any light bulb will fail in service.

The council are anxious that the length of time between changes should be as long as possible, and to this end they have obtained a sample of bulbs from another manufacturer, who claims the same bulb life as their present manufacturer. The council wishes therefore to select the manufacturer whose bulbs have the smallest variance.

When they last tested a random sample of 9 bulbs from their present supplier the summary results were $\sum x = 9415$ hours and $\sum x^2 = 9\,863\,681$, where x represents the lifetime of a bulb.

A random sample of 8 bulbs from the prospective new supplier gave the following bulb lifetimes in hours: 1002, 1018, 943, 1030, 984, 963, 1048, 994.

(a) Calculate unbiased estimates for the means and variances of the two populations.

Assuming that the lifetimes of bulbs are normally distributed,

(b) test at the 10% significance level whether or not the two variances are equal.

(c) State your recommendation to the council, giving reasons for your choice.

3.4 A pooled estimate of variance

Suppose that you take random samples from random variables X and Y that have a common variance σ^2. You will have two estimates of σ^2, namely s_x^2 and s_y^2. A better estimate of σ^2 than either s_x^2 or s_y^2 can be obtained by pooling the two estimates. The question is how should this be done?

You will recall that for a single sample an unbiased estimate of the population variance was obtained by dividing the total sum of squares of the sample by the number of degrees of freedom. Thus

$$s^2 = \frac{\sum (x - \bar{x})^2}{n - 1}$$

is an unbiased estimate of the variance of the population.

A similar idea works for two pooled estimates. You have

$$s_x^2 = \frac{\sum (x - \bar{x}_x)^2}{n_x - 1} \text{ and } s_y^2 = \frac{\sum (x - \bar{x}_y)^2}{n_y - 1}$$

so that $(n_x - 1)\, s_x^2 = \sum (x - \bar{x}_x)^2$ and $(n_y - 1)\, s_y^2 = \sum (x - \bar{x}_y)^2$.

Adding these two sums of squares together to get a total sum of squares gives

$$\sum (x - \bar{x}_x)^2 + \sum (x - \bar{x}_y)^2 = (n_x - 1)\, s_x^2 + (n_y - 1)\, s_y^2$$

and this will have $(n_x - 1) + (n_y - 1)$ degrees of freedom.

Treating the combined samples as a single sample and dividing the total sum of squares by the number of degrees of freedom gives a pooled estimate, s_p^2, of σ^2 thus:

$$s_p^2 = \frac{(n_x - 1)\, s_x^2 + (n_y - 1)\, s_y^2}{(n_x - 1) + (n_y - 1)} = \frac{(n_x - 1)\, s_x^2 + (n_y - 1)\, s_y^2}{n_x + n_y - 2}$$

■ **If a random sample of n_x observations is taken from a normal distribution with unknown variance σ^2 and an independent sample of n_y observations is taken from a normal distribution that also has unknown variance σ^2, then a pooled estimate for σ^2 is**

$$s_p^2 = \frac{(n_x - 1)\, s_x^2 + (n_y - 1)\, s_y^2}{n_x + n_y - 2}$$

where $s_x^2 = \dfrac{\sum x^2 - n_x \bar{x}^2}{n_x - 1}$ **and** $s_y^2 = \dfrac{\sum y^2 - n_y \bar{y}^2}{n_y - 1}$

Notice that if $n_x = n_y = n$ this reduces to

$$s_p^2 = \frac{(n - 1)(s_x^2 + s_y^2)}{2(n - 1)} = \frac{s_x^2 + s_y^2}{2}$$

which is the mean of the two variances. The pooled estimate of variance is really a weighted mean of two variances with the two weights being $(n_x - 1)$ and $(n_y - 1)$.

We can show that S_p^2 is an unbiased estimator as follows:

$$E[(n_x - 1)\, S_x^2 + (n_y - 1)\, S_y^2] = E[(n_x - 1)\, S_x^2] + E[(n_y - 1)\, S_y^2]$$

$$= (n_x - 1)\, \sigma^2 + (n_y - 1)\, \sigma^2$$

$$= [(n_x - 1) + (n_y - 1)]\, \sigma^2$$

so

$$E(S_p^2) = E\left\{ \frac{(n_x - 1)\, S_x^2 + (n_y - 1)\, S_y^2}{(n_x - 1) + (n_y - 1)} \right\}$$

$$= \frac{E[(n_x - 1)\, S_x^2 + (n_y - 1)\, S_y^2]}{[(n_x - 1) + (n_y - 1)]}$$

$$= \frac{[(n_x - 1) + (n_y - 1)]\, \sigma^2}{[(n_x - 1) + (n_y - 1)]}$$

$$= \sigma^2$$

Example 10

A random sample of 15 observations is taken from a population and gives an unbiased estimate for the population variance of 9.47. A second random sample of 12 observations is taken from a different population that has the same population variance as the first population, and gives an unbiased estimate for the variance as 13.84. Calculate an unbiased estimate of the population variance σ^2.

$$s_p^2 = \frac{(n_x - 1)\, s_x^2 + (n_y - 1)\, s_y^2}{(n_x - 1) + (n_y - 1)}$$

$$= \frac{(14 \times 9.47) + (11 \times 13.84)}{14 + 11}$$

$$= 11.3928$$

3.5 Hypothesis test for the difference between the means of two independent normal distributions with unknown variances

You have already seen that if the sample sizes are large then

$$\frac{(\overline{X} - \overline{Y}) - (\mu_x - \mu_y)}{\sqrt{\dfrac{S_x^2}{n_x} + \dfrac{S_y^2}{n_y}}} \approx N(0, 1^2)$$

In this section you will learn how to undertake a difference of means test when the sample sizes are small.

To do this you need to make three assumptions:

1. That the populations are normal.
2. That the samples are independent.
3. That the variances of the two samples are equal.

In general, the third assumption is not an unreasonable one to make. In any case, the equality of the variances can be tested using an F-test as in section 3.3.

The third assumption enables you to use an estimator for the common variance, by pooling the two variances as in section 3.4 to give

$$S_p^2 = \frac{(n_x - 1) S_x^2 + (n_y - 1) S_y^2}{(n_x - 1) + (n_y - 1)}$$

Substituting S_p^2 for S_x^2 and S_y^2 gives

$$\frac{(\bar{X} - \bar{Y}) - (\mu_x - \mu_y)}{\sqrt{\dfrac{S_p^2}{n_x} + \dfrac{S_p^2}{n_y}}} = \frac{(\bar{X} - \bar{Y}) - (\mu_x - \mu_y)}{S_p \sqrt{\dfrac{1}{n_x} + \dfrac{1}{n_y}}}$$

Now, because the sample sizes are small, this will not as before follow a $N(0, 1^2)$ distribution.

You have already seen that in the single-sample case

$$\frac{\bar{X} - \mu_x}{\dfrac{S}{\sqrt{n_x}}}$$

follows a t-distribution, so you will not be surprised to find that

$$\frac{(\bar{X} - \bar{Y}) - (\mu_x - \mu_y)}{S_p \sqrt{\dfrac{1}{n_x} + \dfrac{1}{n_y}}}$$

also follows a t-distribution.

There are $(n_x + n_y)$ in the total sample and two calculated restrictions (namely the means $\bar{X}$ and $\bar{Y}$), so the number of degrees of freedom will be $n_x + n_y - 2$.

■ **If a random sample of n_x observations is taken from a normal distribution that has unknown variance σ^2 and an independent sample of n_y observations is taken from a normal distribution with equal variance, then**

$$\frac{(\bar{X} - \bar{Y}) - (\mu_x - \mu_y)}{S_p \sqrt{\dfrac{1}{n_x} + \dfrac{1}{n_y}}} \sim t_{n_x + n_y - 2} \text{ where } s_p^2 = \frac{(n_x - 1) s_x^2 + (n_y - 1) s_y^2}{n_x + n_y - 2}$$

If you wish to make a two-tailed test remember to halve the significance level so that half is in each tail.

Apart from using the t-distribution rather than the normal distribution for finding the critical values, testing the difference between means of two independent normal distributions with unknown variances follows similar steps to those used for testing the difference of means when the variances were known.

The following steps might help you in answering questions on the difference of means of normal distributions when the variances are unknown.

1.   Write down the null (H_0).
2.   Write down the alternative hypothesis (H_1).
3.   Specify α.
4.   Find the critical value from the tables for $t_{n_x + n_y - 2}$.
5.   Write down the critical region.
6.   Calculate the sample means and variances $\bar{x}$, $\bar{y}$, s_x^2 and s_y^2.

Calculate a pooled estimate of the variance:

$$s_p^2 = \frac{(n_x - 1)\, s_x^2 + (n_y - 1)\, s_y^2}{(n_x - 1) + (n_y - 1)}$$

Calculate the value of

$$\frac{(\bar{X} - \bar{Y}) - (\mu_x - \mu_y)}{S_p\sqrt{\dfrac{1}{n_x} + \dfrac{1}{n_y}}}$$

7.   Complete the test and state your conclusions. The following points should be addressed:
     (a) is the result significant,
     (b) what are the implications in terms of the original problem?

Example 11

Two groups of students X and Y were taught by different teachers. At the end of their course a random sample of students from each class was selected and given a test. The test results out of 50 were as follows:

Group X 40 37 45 34 30 41 42 43 36
Group Y 38 43 36 45 35 44 41

The head teacher wishes to find out if there is a significant difference between the results for these two groups.

(a) What assumptions need to be made in order to conduct a difference of means test on this data?

(b) Assuming that these assumptions apply, test at the 10% significance level whether or not there is a significant difference between the means.

(a) You must assume that the two samples come from normal distributions, that they are independent, and that the populations from which they are taken have the same variances.

(b) Using a calculator gives $n_x = 9$, $\bar{x} = 38.667$, $s_x^2 = 23.0$, $n_y = 7$, $\bar{y} = 40.286$, $s_y^2 = 15.9$.

$$s_p^2 = \frac{(n_x - 1) s_x^2 + (n_y - 1) s_y^2}{n_x + n_y - 2}$$

$$= \frac{(8 \times 23.0) + (6 \times 15.9)}{9 + 7 - 2}$$

$$= 19.957$$

So $$s_p = 4.467$$

$$H_0 : \mu_x = \mu_y, \quad H_1 : \mu_x \neq \mu_y$$

$$t = \frac{|(\bar{x} - \bar{y})|}{s_p \sqrt{\dfrac{1}{n_x} + \dfrac{1}{n_y}}}$$

$\boxed{\text{Note } \mu_x - \mu_y = 0}$

$$= \frac{40.286 - 38.667}{4.467 \sqrt{\dfrac{1}{9} + \dfrac{1}{7}}}$$

$$= 0.719$$

Critical value $t_{n_x + n_y - 2}$ (5%) $= t_{14}$ (5%) is 1.761 (two-tailed test so 5% at each tail).

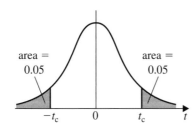

The critical regions are $t \leqslant -1.761$ and $t \geqslant 1.761$.

$-1.761 < 0.719 < 1.761$ so the result is not significant. On the evidence given by the two samples there is no difference between the means of the two groups.

Example 12

A random sample of the heights, in cm, of sixth form boys and girls was taken, with the following results:

Boys' heights   152, 148, 147, 157, 158, 140, 141, 144
Girls' heights   142, 146, 132, 125, 138, 131, 143

(a) Carry out a two-sample t-test at the 5% significance level on these data to see whether the mean height of boys exceeds the mean height of girls by 4 cm.
(b) State any assumptions that you have made.

Let x be the height of a boy and y the height of a girl.

(a) $H_0 : \mu_x = \mu_y + 4$ $H_1 : \mu_x > \mu_y + 4$

Critical value $t_{n_x + n_y - 2} = t_{13}(5\%) = 1.771$.

The critical region is $t \geqslant 1.771$

Using a calculator gives
for the boys $\bar{x} = 148.375$, $s_x^2 = 46.554$, $n_x = 8$,
for the girls $\bar{y} = 136.714$, $s_y^2 = 57.905$, $n_y = 7$.

$$s_p = \frac{(n_x - 1)s_x^2 + (n_y - 1)s_y^2}{n_x + n_y - 2}$$

$$= \frac{(7 \times 46.554) + (6 \times 57.905)}{8 + 7 - 2}$$

$$= 51.793$$

So $s_p = 7.197$

$$t = \frac{|(\bar{x} - \bar{y})| - (\mu_x - \mu_y)}{s_p\sqrt{\dfrac{1}{n_x} + \dfrac{1}{n_y}}}$$

$$= \frac{(148.375 - 136.714) - 4}{7.197\sqrt{\frac{1}{8} + \frac{1}{7}}}$$

$$= 2.057$$

2.057 is in the critical region and so there is sufficient evidence to reject the null hypothesis. The mean height of boys exceeds the mean height of girls by 4 cm.
(b) The assumptions made are that the two samples are independent, that the variances of both populations are equal and that the populations are normally distributed.

Selecting the correct test

There are several different difference of means tests. You should be aware of the circumstances under which each is used.

The table below shows these:

Distributions	Variances	Sample sizes	Test statistic
Normal	Known	Any	$$\dfrac{(\overline{X}-\overline{Y})-(\mu_x-\mu_y)}{\sqrt{\dfrac{\sigma_x^2}{n_x}+\dfrac{\sigma_y^2}{n_y}}}\sim \mathrm{N}(0,1)$$
Not normal	Known	Large	$$\dfrac{(\overline{X}-\overline{Y})-(\mu_x-\mu_y)}{\sqrt{\dfrac{\sigma_x^2}{n_x}+\dfrac{\sigma_y^2}{n_y}}}\sim \mathrm{N}(0,1)$$
Normal	Unknown but assumed equal	Any	$$\dfrac{(\overline{X}-\overline{Y})-(\mu_x-\mu_y)}{S_\mathrm{p}\sqrt{\dfrac{1}{n_x}+\dfrac{1}{n_y}}}\sim t_{n_x+n_y-2}$$

3.6 Confidence interval for the difference between two means from independent normal distributions with equal but unknown variances

You have already seen that if you assume that two samples come from normal distributions, that they are independent and that the populations from which they are taken have the same variances

$$\frac{(\bar{x}-\bar{y})-(\mu_x-\mu_y)}{s_\mathrm{p}\sqrt{\dfrac{1}{n_x}+\dfrac{1}{n_y}}}\sim t_{n_x+n_y-2} \quad \text{where } s_\mathrm{p}^2=\frac{(n_x-1)s_x^2+(n_y-1)s_y^2}{n_x+n_y-2}$$

As before, with confidence intervals you normally expect the interval to be symmetrical, so you split the remainder between the two tails. For example, if you wish to have a 95% interval, the remaining 5% is split equally between the two tails to give $2\frac{1}{2}\%$ in each tail.

The tables will then give you the value of t that is exceeded with 2.5% probability (or 5% for a 90% confidence interval). If you write t_c for the relevant value then

$$P(-t_c < t_{n_x + n_y - 2} < t_c) = 0.95 \text{ (or 0.09)}$$

$$P\left(-t_c < \frac{(\bar{x} - \bar{y}) - (\mu_x - \mu_y)}{s_p \sqrt{\dfrac{1}{n_x} + \dfrac{1}{n_y}}} < t_c\right) = 0.95 \text{ (or 0.09)}$$

$$P\left(-t_c s_p \sqrt{\frac{1}{n_x} + \frac{1}{n_y}} < (\bar{x} - \bar{y}) - (\mu_x - \mu_y) < t_c s_p \sqrt{\frac{1}{n_x} + \frac{1}{n_y}}\right) = 0.95 \text{ (or 0.09)}$$

The confidence limits for $(\mu_x - \mu_y)$ are therefore given by

$$(\bar{x} - \bar{y}) \pm t_c s_p \sqrt{\frac{1}{n_x} + \frac{1}{n_y}}$$

and the confidence interval is

$$\left\{ (\bar{x} - \bar{y}) - t_c s_p \sqrt{\frac{1}{n_x} + \frac{1}{n_y}}, \ (\bar{x} - \bar{y}) + t_c s_p \sqrt{\frac{1}{n_x} + \frac{1}{n_y}} \right\}$$

■ **The confidence limits for the difference between two means from independent normal distributions, X and Y, when the variances are equal but unknown are given by**

$$(\bar{x} - \bar{y}) \pm t_c s_p \sqrt{\frac{1}{n_x} + \frac{1}{n_y}}$$

where s_p is the pooled estimate of the population variance, and t_c is the relevant value taken from the t-distribution tables.

The confidence interval is given by

$$\left\{ (\bar{x} - \bar{y}) - t_c s_p \sqrt{\frac{1}{n_x} + \frac{1}{n_y}}, \ (\bar{x} - \bar{y}) + t_c s_p \sqrt{\frac{1}{n_x} + \frac{1}{n_y}} \right\}$$

Example 13

In a survey on the petrol consumption of cars a random sample of 12 cars with 2 litre engines was compared with a random sample of 15 cars with 1.6 litre engines. The following results show the consumption, in suitable units, of the cars:

2 litre cars: 34.4, 32.1, 30.1, 32.8, 31.5, 35.8, 28.2, 26.6, 28.8, 28.5, 33.6, 28.8

1.6 litre cars: 35.3, 34.0, 36.7, 40.9, 34.4, 39.8, 33.6, 36.7, 34.0, 39.2, 39.8, 38.7, 40.8, 35.0, 36.7

Calculate a 95% confidence interval for the difference between the two mean petrol consumption figures. You may assume that the variables are normally distributed and that they have the same variance.

For the 2 litre engine $n_y = 12$, $\bar{y} = 30.933$, $s_y^2 = 8.177$.

For the 1.6 litre engine $n_x = 15$, $\bar{x} = 37.04$, $s_x^2 = 6.894$.

$$
\begin{aligned}
s_p^2 &= \frac{(n_x - 1)s_x^2 + (n_y - 1)s_y^2}{n_x + n_y - 2} \\
&= \frac{(14 \times 6.894) + (11 \times 8.177)}{25} \\
&= 7.459 \\
s_p &= \sqrt{7.459} = 2.731 \\
t_c &= t_{25}(2.5\%) = 2.060
\end{aligned}
$$

The confidence limits are

$$
\begin{aligned}
(\bar{x} - \bar{y}) \pm t_c s_p \sqrt{\frac{1}{n_x} + \frac{1}{n_y}} &= (37.04 - 30.933) \pm \left(2.060 \times 2.731 \sqrt{\frac{1}{15} + \frac{1}{12}} \right) \\
&= 6.107 \pm 2.179 \\
&= 8.286 \text{ and } 3.928
\end{aligned}
$$

The 95% confidence interval is (3.928, 8.286).

Exercise 3C

1 A random sample of size 20 from a normal population gave $\bar{x} = 16$, $s^2 = 12$.

A second sample of 11 from a normal population gave $\bar{x} = 14$, $s^2 = 12$.

(a) Assuming that both populations have the same variance, find an unbiased estimate for that variance.

(b) Test at the 5% significance level the suggestion that the two populations have the same mean.

2 Salmon reared in Scottish fish farms are generally larger than wild salmon. A fisherman measured the length of the first 6 wild salmon caught on his beat. Their lengths in cm were

$$42.8, 40.0, 38.2, 37.5, 37.0, 36.5$$

Chefs prefer wild salmon to fish-farmed salmon because of their better flavour. A chef was offered 4 salmon that were claimed to be wild. Their lengths in cm were

$$42, 43.0, 41.5, 40.0$$

Use the information given above and a suitable t-test at the 5% significance level to help the chef to decide if the claim is likely to be correct. You may assume that the populations are normally distributed.

3 In order to check the effectiveness of three drugs against the *E. coli* bacillus, 15 cultures of the bacillus (5 for each of 3 different antibiotics) had discs soaked in the antibiotics placed in their centre. The 15 cultures were left for a time and the area in cm^2 per microgram of drug where the *E. coli* was killed was measured. The results for three different drugs are given below:

Streptomycin: 0.210, 0.252, 0.251, 0.210, 0.256, 0.253
Tetracycline: 0.123, 0.090, 0.123, 0.141, 0.142, 0.092
Erythromycin: 0.134, 0.120, 0.123, 0.210, 0.134, 0.134

(a) It was thought that Tetracycline and Erythromycin seemed equally effective. Assuming that the populations are normally distributed, test this at the 5% significance level.
(b) Streptomycin was thought to be more effective than either of the others. Treating the other 2 as being a single sample of 12, test this assertion at the same level of significance.

4 A random sample of 10 toothed winkles was taken from a sheltered shore, and a sample of 15 was taken from a non-sheltered shore. The maximum basal width (x mm) of the shells was measured and the results are summarised below.

Sheltered shore: $\bar{x} = 25$, $s^2 = 4$. Non-sheltered shore: $\bar{x} = 22$, $s^2 = 5.3$.
(a) Find a 95% confidence interval for the difference between the means.
(b) State an assumption that you have made when calculating this interval.

5 A packet of plant seeds was sown and, when the seeds had germinated and begun to grow, 8 were transferred into pots containing a soil-less compost and 10 were grown in a soil-based compost. After 6 weeks of growth the heights, x, in cm of the plants were measured, with the following results:

Soil-less compost: 9.3, 8.7, 7.8, 10.0, 9.2, 9.5, 7.9, 8.9
Soil-based compost: 12.8, 13.1, 11.2, 10.1, 13.1, 12.0, 12.5, 11.7, 11.9, 12.0

Assuming that the populations are normally distributed,

(a) Use a difference of means test at the 5% significance level to test the suggestion that the plants grow better in the soil-based compost.

(b) Assuming that there is a difference between the two means calculate a 90% confidence interval for this difference.

3.7 The paired *t*-test

There are many occasions on which you might want to compare results before and after some treatment, or the efficiency of two different types of treatment. You could, for example, be investigating the effect of alcohol on people's reactions, or the difference in intelligence levels of identical twins who were separated at birth and who have been brought up in different family circumstances.

In both cases you need to have a common link between the two sets of results, for instance by taking the same person's result before and after drinking alcohol, or by the twins being identical. It is necessary to have this link so that differences caused by other factors are eliminated as much as possible. It would, for example, be of little use if you tested one person's reactions without drinking alcohol against a different person's reactions after drinking alcohol, because any difference could be due to normal variations in their reactions. In the same way you would have to use identical twins in the intelligence experiment, otherwise any difference in intelligence might be due to the normal variance of intelligence between different people. In these cases each result in one of the samples is paired with a result in the other sample; the results are therefore referred to as **paired**.

In paired experiments such as these you are not really interested in the individual results as such, but in the difference, D, between the results. In these circumstances you can treat the differences between pairs of matched subjects as if they were a random sample from a $N(\mu, \sigma^2)$ distribution. You can then proceed as you did for a single sample on page 41.

In Statistics 3 you saw that if n observations are taken from a $N(\mu, \sigma^2)$ distribution, the sample mean will follow a $N\left(\mu, \dfrac{\sigma^2}{n}\right)$ distribution.

If you take as a null hypothesis that there is no difference between the results, then you would expect the mean of the differences $\bar{D}$ to be zero, that is to say $\bar{D}$ will then follow a $N\left(0, \dfrac{\sigma^2}{n}\right)$ distribution under H_0.

Note that although you do not need to assume that the two populations are normal, you do need to assume that the differences are normally distributed, or if you knew σ^2 (which is very unlikely) the central limit theorem would be sufficient.

If you do not know the value of σ^2 you will have to use S^2, and then as you saw from section 2.2,

$$t = \frac{(\bar{D} - \mu_D)}{\dfrac{S}{\sqrt{n}}} \sim t_{n-1}$$

Taking $H_0 : \mu_D = 0$ as your null hypothesis this reduces to

$$t = \frac{\bar{D} - 0}{\dfrac{S}{\sqrt{n}}} \sim t_{n-1}$$

■ **In a paired experiment with a mean of the differences between the samples of $\bar{D}$**

$$\frac{\bar{D} - \mu_D}{\dfrac{S}{\sqrt{n}}} \sim t_{n-1}$$

The paired t-test proceeds in almost the same way as the t-test itself. The steps are written below.

1. Write down the null hypothesis H_0.
2. Write down the alternative hypothesis H_1.
3. Specify α.
4. Write down the degrees of freedom (remembering that $v = n - 1$).
5. Write down the critical region.
6. Calculate the differences d.
Calculate $\bar{d}$ and s^2.
Calculate the value of the test statistic

$$t = \frac{\bar{d} - \mu_D}{\dfrac{s}{\sqrt{n}}}$$

7. Complete the test and state your conclusions. As before, the following points should be addressed:
   (a) Is the result significant or not?
   (b) What are the implications in terms of the original problem?

Example 14

In an experiment to test the effects of alcohol on the reaction times of people, a group of 10 students took part in an experiment. The students were asked to react to a light going on by pushing a switch that would switch it off again. Their reaction times were automatically recorded. After the students had drunk one pint of beer the experiment was repeated. The results are shown below:

Student	A	B	C	D	E	F	G	H	I	J
Reaction time before (seconds)	0.8	0.2	0.4	0.6	0.4	0.6	0.4	0.8	1.0	0.9
Reaction time after (seconds)	0.7	0.5	0.6	0.8	0.8	0.6	0.7	0.9	1.0	0.7
Difference	−0.1	0.3	0.2	0.2	0.4	0	0.3	0.1	0	−0.2

Test at the 5% significance level whether or not the consumption of a pint of beer increased the students' reaction times.

$$\frac{\sum d}{n} = \frac{1.2}{10} = 0.12$$

$$s^2 = \frac{\sum d^2 - n\bar{d}^2}{n-1}$$

$$= \frac{0.48 - 10(0.12)^2}{9}$$

$$= 0.037\,333\,3$$

$$H_0 : \mu_D = 0 \quad H_1 : \mu_D > 0$$

test statistic $$t = \frac{\bar{d}}{\dfrac{s}{\sqrt{n}}} = \frac{0.12}{\dfrac{0.1932\ldots}{\sqrt{10}}} = 1.9640$$

t_9 (5%) critical value is 1.833.

1.9641 > 1.833. The result is significant. There is evidence that a pint of beer increases student reaction times.

Example 15

In order to compare two methods of measuring the hardness of metals, readings of Brinell hardness were taken using each method for 8 different metal specimens. The resulting Brinell hardness readings are given in the table below:

Material	Reading method A	Reading method B
Aluminium	29	31
Magnesium alloy	64	63
Wrought iron	104	105
Duralumin	116	119
Mild steel	138	140
70/30 brass	156	156
Cast iron	199	200
Nickel chrome steel	385	386

(a) Use a paired *t*-test, at the 5% significance level, to test whether or not there is a difference in the readings given by the two methods.

The differences are 2, −1, 1, 3, 2, 0, 1 and 1.

$$H_0 : \mu_d = 0 \quad H_1 : \mu_d \neq 0$$

$$\frac{\sum d}{n} = \frac{9}{8} = 1.125 \quad \sum d^2 = 21$$

$$s^2 = \frac{\sum d^2 - n\bar{d}^2}{n-1}$$

$$= \frac{21 - 8(1.125)^2}{7}$$

$$= 1.554$$

test statistic

$$t = \frac{\bar{d}}{\dfrac{s}{\sqrt{n}}}$$

$$= \frac{1.125}{\dfrac{\sqrt{1.554}}{\sqrt{8}}}$$

$$= 2.553$$

t_7 (2.5%) critical value is 2.365.

The critical regions are $t < -2.365$ and $t > 2.365$.

Now 2.553 is in the critical region, so the result is significant; there is sufficient evidence to reject the null hypothesis. There is a difference between the two methods.

Exercise 3D

1 It is claimed that completion of a shorthand course has increased the shorthand speeds of the students.

(a) If the suggestion that the mean speed of the students has not altered is to be tested, write down suitable hypotheses for which (i) a two-tailed test is appropriate, and (ii) a one-tailed test is appropriate.

The table below gives the shorthand speeds of students before and after the course:

Student	A	B	C	D	E	F
Speed before in words/min	35	40	28	45	30	32
Speed after	42	45	28	45	40	40

(b) Carry out a paired *t*-test, at the 5% significance level, to determine whether or not there has been an increase in shorthand speeds.

2 A large number of students took two General Studies papers that were supposed to be of equal difficulty. The results for 10 students chosen at random are shown below:

Candidate	A	B	C	D	E	F	G	H	I	J
Paper 1	18	25	40	10	38	20	25	35	18	43
Paper 2	20	27	39	12	40	23	20	35	20	41

The teacher looked at the marks of the random sample of 10 students, and decided that paper 2 was easier than paper 1.

Given that the marks on each paper are normally distributed, carry out an appropriate test, at the 1% significance level.

3 It is claimed by the manufacturer that by chewing a special flavoured chewing gum smokers are able to reduce their craving for cigarettes, and thus cut down on the number of cigarettes smoked per day. In a trial of the gum on a random selection of 10 people the no-gum smoking rate and the smoking rate when chewing the gum were investigated, with the following results:

Person	A	B	C	D	E	F	G	H	I	J
Without gum smoking rate cigs/day	20	35	40	32	45	15	22	30	34	40
With gum smoking rate cigs/day	15	25	35	30	45	15	14	25	28	34

(a) Use a paired *t*-test at the 5% significance level to test the manufacturer's claim.

(b) State any assumptions you have had to make.

4 The council of Somewhere town are going to put a new traffic management scheme into operation in the hope that it will make travel to work in the mornings quicker for most people. Before the scheme is put into operation, 10 randomly selected workers are asked to record the time it takes them to come into work on a Wednesday morning. After the scheme is put into place, the same 10 workers are again asked to record the time it takes them to come into work on a particular Wednesday morning.

The times in minutes are shown in the table below:

Worker	A	B	C	D	E	F	G	H	I	J
Before	23	37	53	42	39	60	54	85	46	38
After	18	35	49	42	34	48	52	79	37	37

Test at the 5% significance level whether or not the journey time to work has decreased.

5 A teacher is anxious to test the idea that students' results in mock examinations are good predictors for their results in actual examinations. He selects 8 students at random from those doing a mock Statistics examination and records their marks out of 100; later he collects the same students' marks in the actual examination. The resulting marks are as follows:

Student	A	B	C	D	E	F	G	H
Mock examination mark	35	86	70	91	45	64	78	38
Actual examination	45	77	81	86	53	71	68	46

(a) Use a paired *t*-test to investigate whether or not the mock examination is a good predictor. (Use a 10% significance level.)

(b) State any assumptions you have made.

6 The manager of a dress-making company took a random sample of 10 of his employees and recorded the number of dresses made by each. He discovered that the number of dresses made between 3.00 and 5.00 p.m. was fewer than the same employees achieved between 9.00 and 11.00 a.m. He wondered if a tea break from 2.45 to 3.00 p.m. would increase productivity during these last two hours of the day.

The number of dresses made by these workers in the last two hours of the day before and after the introduction of the tea break were as shown below:

Worker	A	B	C	D	E	F	G	H	I	J
Before	75	73	75	81	74	73	77	75	75	72
After	80	84	79	84	85	84	78	78	80	83

(a) Why was the comparison made for the same ten workers?

(b) Conduct, at the 5% significance level, a paired t-test to see if the introduction of a tea break has increased production between 3.00 and 5.00 p.m.

SUMMARY OF KEY POINTS

1 For a random sample of size n_x observations from $N(\mu_x, \sigma_x^2)$ and an independent random sample of n_y observations from $N(\mu_y, \sigma_y^2)$

$$\frac{S_x^2/\sigma_x^2}{S_y^2/\sigma_y^2} \sim F_{n_x - 1, \, n_y - 1}$$

2
$$F_{v_2, v_1} = \frac{1}{F_{v_1, v_2}}$$

3 If a random sample of n_x observations is taken from a normal distribution with unknown variance σ^2 and an independent sample of n_y observations is taken from a normal distribution that also has unknown variance σ^2, then a pooled estimate for σ^2 is

$$s_p^2 = \frac{(n_x - 1)s_x^2 + (n_y - 1)s_y^2}{n_x + n_y - 2}$$

4 If a random sample of n_x observations is taken from a normal distribution that has an unknown variance σ^2 and an independent sample of n_y observations is taken from a normal distribution with equal variance, then

$$\frac{(\bar{X} - \bar{Y}) - (\mu_x - \mu_y)}{S_p\sqrt{\dfrac{1}{n_x} + \dfrac{1}{n_y}}} \sim t_{n_x + n_y - 2}$$

5 The 95% confidence interval for the difference between two means from independent normal distributions X and Y that have equal but unknown variances is

$$\left((\bar{x} - \bar{y}) - t_{n_x + n_y - 2}(0.025) \times s_p\sqrt{\dfrac{1}{n_x} + \dfrac{1}{n_y}}, \right.$$

$$\left. (\bar{x} - \bar{y}) + t_{n_x + n_y - 2}(0.025) \times s_p\sqrt{\dfrac{1}{n_x} + \dfrac{1}{n_y}} \right)$$

The 90% confidence interval for the difference between two means from independent normal distributions X and Y that have equal but unknown variances is

$$\left((\bar{x} - \bar{y}) - t_{n_x + n_y - 2}(0.05) \times s_p \sqrt{\frac{1}{n_x} + \frac{1}{n_y}}, \right.$$

$$\left. (\bar{x} - \bar{y}) + t_{n_x + n_y - 2}(0.05) \times s_p \sqrt{\frac{1}{n_x} + \frac{1}{n_y}} \right)$$

6 In a paired experiment with a mean of the differences between the samples of $\bar{D}$

$$\frac{\bar{D} - \mu_D}{\dfrac{S}{\sqrt{n}}} \sim t_{n-1}$$

Review exercise 2

1 Random samples are taken from two normally distributed populations.

The first sample gives the following summary statistics:

$$n_1 = 25, \ s_1^2 = 48.3$$

The second sample gives

$$n_2 = 17, \ s_2^2 = 42.1$$

Test at the 5% significance level $H_0 : \sigma_1^2 = \sigma_2^2$ against $H_1 : \sigma_1^2 > \sigma_2^2$.

2 A random sample of 8 apples taken from variety A had the following weights in grams:

$$115, \ 112, \ 121, \ 114, \ 113, \ 114, \ 108, \ 110$$

A random sample of apples from variety B gave the following summary statistics:

$$\bar{x} = 111.1, \ s^2 = 19.350, \ n = 11$$

Test at the 10% significance level whether or not the two varieties have the same variance. State any assumptions you have had to make in order to carry out this test.

3 A garage sells petrol at 83 pence a litre and during a particular week a random sample of 18 customers bought a mean amount of 32 litres, with a standard deviation, S, of 10 litres. After petrol was increased in price to 87 pence a litre, a similar study of 18 randomly selected customers gave a mean figure of 26 litres with a variance, S^2, of 92.

Assuming that the amount of petrol sold to each customer is normally distributed, and using a 5% significance level, test whether or not the mean amount of petrol sold per customer had decreased.

4 An experiment was carried out to see if a person's reactions were quicker in the morning than in the evening. A random sample of 15 people, selected at random, were given a test in the morning, and a similar test in the evening. Their reaction times, in milliseconds, were recorded as follows:

Person	A	B	C	D	E	F	G	H	I	J	K	L	M	N	O
Morning	3.2	3.8	4.0	3.1	2.6	2.8	3.3	3.1	3.6	3.7	3.8	4.2	4.1	3.2	3.0
Afternoon	3.3	3.8	4.3	3.0	2.6	2.5	3.8	3.3	3.8	3.6	3.9	4.2	4.3	3.6	3.1

(a) Explain why a paired t-test would be used in this case.
(b) Test at the 5% level of significance whether or not people's reactions are slower in the evenings than in the mornings.

5 The manufacturer of 'Gleam' toothpaste claims that children who use their product will have fewer dental cavities than those using 'Sparkle' toothpaste.
In a carefully supervised study 11 pairs of identical twins used the two products – one twin using 'Gleam' toothpaste and the other 'Sparkle'. After a period of time the number of cavities for each child was recorded, the results being given below:

Twins	A	B	C	D	E	F	G	H	I	J	K
'Gleam'	1	2	0	3	0	2	1	3	1	2	1
'Sparkle'	3	1	2	4	1	5	0	5	2	4	3

(a) Explain why identical twins were used for this experiment.
(b) Conduct a paired t-test at the 5% significance level to test whether or not the manufacturer's claim is justified.

6 A manufacturer of a petrol additive claims that adding it to petrol causes the car to do more miles to the gallon. A trial was set up with 8 pairs of cars, each car in a pair being identical, one car in the pair using the additive and the other not. The number of miles done on one gallon of fuel was recorded for each car, the results being as follows:

Car type	A	B	C	D	E	F	G	H
Without additive	32	37	35	31	30	33	32	34
With additive	36	34	38	37	33	38	38	32

Conduct, at the 5% significance level, a paired t-test to examine the manufacturer's claim.

7 A large bank has branches in the North of England and also in the South. A random sample of 15 past employees in their northern branches was compared for length of service with a random sample of 15 in their southern branches. The number of years, X, the employees stayed with the bank before leaving for other jobs was summarised as follows:

For the South $\sum x_S^2 = 86, \sum x_S = 24.$

For the North $\sum x_N^2 = 126, \sum x_N = 30.$

Conduct, at the 5% significance level, a test to see whether the mean number of years employees stayed in a job was greater in the North than in the South.

8 The random variable X has an F distribution with 2 and 7 degrees of freedom.
Find $P(X < 9.55)$. [E]

9 The random variable X follows an F distribution with 6 and 12 degrees of freedom.
(a) Show that $P(0.25 < X < 3.00) = 0.9$.
A large number of values are randomly selected from an F distribution with 6 and 12 degrees of freedom.
(b) Find the probability that the seventh value to be selected will be the third value to lie between 0.25 and 3.00 [E]

10 The variance of the lengths of a sample of 9 tent poles produced by a machine was $63 \, mm^2$. A second machine produced a sample of 13 tent poles with a variance of $225 \, mm^2$. Both these values are unbiased estimates of the population variances.
(a) Test, at the 10% level, whether there is evidence that the machines differ in variability, stating the null and alternative hypotheses.
(b) State the assumption you have made about the distribution of the populations in order to carry out the test in part (a). [E]

11 The closing balances, £x, of a number of randomly chosen bank current accounts of two different types, Chegrit and Dicabalk, are analysed by a statistician. The summary statistics are given in the table below:

	Sample size	$\sum x$	$\sum x^2$
Chegrit	7	276	143 742
Dicabalk	15	394	102 341

Stating clearly your hypotheses, test at the 10% significance level whether or not the two distributions have the same variance. (You may assume that the closing balances of each type of account are normally distributed.) [E]

12 Machinery is supplied to a factory with parts already assembled, and secured by nuts and bolts. For the nut-and-bolt pairs, the effective diameter of the bolt should be on average 0.6 mm less than that of its nut. The diameters of the nuts and the bolts may be assumed to follow a normal distribution. A quality control engineer suspected that the difference between the diameters of a batch of nuts and their bolts was too great, and she recorded the data shown in the table:

Assembly no.	1	2	3	4
Diameter of bolt (mm)	4.03	4.08	4.00	4.00
Diameter of nut (mm)	4.75	4.88	4.90	5.01

Test at the 5% level whether there is any evidence for the engineer's suspicions, stating the null and alternative hypotheses. [E]

13 As part of an exercise to determine whether A-level Mathematics examinations were of the same standard when set by two different examining boards, 10 candidates were given special permission to sit the examination with both boards at the same session.
Their marks are shown in the table:

Candidate	1	2	3	4	5	6	7	8	9	10
Board L	90	90	87	43	32	75	21	64	69	52
Board M	91	84	79	47	29	78	22	51	56	48

Earlier analyses have confirmed that the marks on examinations of this type are approximately normally distributed. Using an appropriate test, determine whether there is evidence at the 5% level of a difference in standards between the boards, stating the null and alternative hypotheses. [E]

14 A random sample of 10 new clients at a weight-watchers class were weighed on arrival at their enrolment session and their weights, in kg, were recorded.

After several weeks these same 10 clients were weighed again and their weights were recorded. The initial and final weights are given in the table below:

Client	1	2	3	4	5	6	7	8	9	10
Initial weight	90.7	63.1	72.4	65.3	101.8	92.7	86.4	76.9	95.7	80.8
Final weight	87.1	63.2	70.2	60.1	100.2	85.2	86.4	72.5	90.0	80.2

Assuming the observations are normally distributed, test whether or not there has been a mean loss in weight. Use a 5% level of significance and state your hypotheses clearly. [E]

15 Forty children were randomly selected from all 12-year-old children in a large city to compare two methods of teaching the spelling of 50 words which were likely to be unfamiliar to the children. Twenty children were randomly allocated to each method. Six weeks later the children were tested to see how many of the words they could spell correctly. The summary statistics for the two methods are given in the table below, where $\bar{x}$ is the mean number of words spelt correctly, s^2 is an unbiased estimate of the variance of the number of words spelt correctly and n is the number of children taught using each method:

	$\bar{x}$	s^2	n
Method A	32.7	6.1^2	20
Method B	38.2	5.2^2	20

(a) Calculate a 99% confidence interval for the difference between the mean numbers of words spelt correctly by children who used Method B and Method A.

(b) State two assumptions you have made in carrying out part (a).

(c) Interpret your result.   [E]

16 A drug administered in tablet form to help people sleep and a placebo were given for two weeks to a random sample of eight patients in a clinic. The drug and the placebo were given in random order for one week each. The average number of hours' sleep that each patient had per night with the drug and with the placebo are given in the table below:

Patient	1	2	3	4	5	6	7	8
Hours of sleep with drug	10.5	6.7	8.9	6.7	9.2	10.9	11.9	7.6
Hours of sleep with placebo	10.3	6.5	9.0	5.3	8.7	7.5	9.3	7.2

Test, at the 1% level of significance, whether or not the drug increases the mean number of hours' sleep per night. State your hypotheses clearly.   [E]

17 To test whether a new version of a computer programming language enabled faster task completion, the same task was performed by 16 programmers, divided at random into two groups. The first group used the new version of the language, and the time for task completion, in hours, for each programmer was as follows:

$$4.9 \quad 6.3 \quad 9.6 \quad 5.2 \quad 4.1 \quad 7.2 \quad 4.0$$

The second group used the old version, and their times were summarised as follows:

$$n = 9, \ \sum x = 71.2, \ \sum x^2 = 604.92$$

(a) State the null and alternative hypotheses.

(b) Perform an appropriate test at the 5% level of significance.

In order to compare like with like, experiments such as this
are often performed using the same individuals in the first and
the second groups.

(c) Give a reason why this strategy would not be appropriate
in this case.   [E]

18 A manufacturer of a petrol additive claims that adding a dose
of the additive to a tankful of petrol improves petrol
consumption under virtually all driving conditions.
The average fuel consumption figures, in miles per gallon, for
9 different motorists for a tankful of petrol without the
additive were

29, 32, 35, 25, 39, 28, 29, 34, 33

The average fuel consumption figures for the same 9 motorists
for a tankful of petrol with the additive, and given in the same
order, were

33, 35, 34, 26, 41, 31, 30, 32, 32

(a) Use a suitable t-test to determine whether the
manufacturer's claim can be supported, using a 5%
significance level. State clearly your null hypothesis and the
conclusion of your test.

(b) State an assumption which must be made to justify the use
of this test.
A friend uses the same data to test the same hypothesis at the
10% level of significance.

(c) State the conclusion your friend should draw.

(d) Comment on your answers to (a) and (c).   [E]

19 The mean daily consumption of cigarettes by a random sample
of smokers before and after their attendance at an anti-
smoking workshop is given in the following table:

Smoker	A	B	C	D	E	F	G	H	I	J
Before workshop	32	15	13	17	19	21	110	16	23	13
After workshop	20	20	12	10	6	10	120	8	19	22

(a) Explain why you would be cautious about using a test to
analyse these data.

It was later found that the figures for smoker G had been weekly figures not daily ones, and that these figures had been stated in the wrong order. The correct values were 17 cigarettes per day before the workshop and 16 cigarettes per day after the workshop.

(b) Stating any assumption you make, use an appropriate test to determine whether or not the daily consumption has reduced as a result of the workshop. State clearly your hypotheses and use a 5% level of significance.

Two further random samples each of 10 smokers who attended the anti-smoking workshop were selected. For each member of the first sample the mean daily consumption *before* the workshop was recorded. For each member of the second sample the mean daily consumption *after* the workshop was recorded.

The table below shows summary statistics for the mean daily consumption before and after the workshop with $\bar{x}$ representing the means and s^2 representing the unbiased estimates of population variance in each case:

	$\bar{x}$	s^2
Mean daily consumption before the workshop	18.6	32.488
Mean daily consumption after the workshop	14.3	33.344

(c) Stating clearly any assumption you make, calculate a 90% confidence interval for the difference in the mean daily consumption of cigarettes before and after the workshop.   [E]

20 A farmer had a herd of 15 goats for milking. The milk yield from the herd, in coded units, was summarised by

$$\sum x = 144, \ \sum x^2 = 1474.$$

After a year, the farmer changed his animal feed supplier, and wished to find whether there was a difference in the yield of milk with the new feed. By this time, however, one goat had died, and another had been sold. Four other young goats had reached maturity and had been added to the herd, so the herd consisted of 17 goats. The milk yield, in the same units, was summarised by

$$\sum y = 183, \ \sum y^2 = 2065.$$

The farmer decided to perform a two-sample t-test at the 5% level.

(a) Perform this test, stating the null and alternative hypotheses.

(b) State two assumptions which must be satisfied for this test to be valid.

(c) State why this test is invalid.

(d) Suggest an alternative strategy for the farmer to use, which would be statistically valid. [E]

21 A company undertakes investigations to compare the fuel consumption, x, in miles per gallon, of two different cars, the Volcera and the Spintono, with a view to purchasing a number as company cars.

For a random sample of 12 Volceras the fuel consumption is summarised by

$$\sum x = 384 \ \text{and} \ \sum x^2 = 12\,480$$

A statistician incorrectly combines the figures for the sample of 12 Volceras with those of a random sample of 15 Spintonos, then carries out calculations as if they are all one larger sample and obtains the results $\bar{x} = 34$ and $s^2 = 23$.

(a) Show that, for the sample of 15 Spintonos, $\sum x = 534$ and $\sum x^2 = 19\,330$.

Given that the variance of the fuel consumption for each make of car is σ^2,

(b) obtain an unbiased estimate for σ^2.

(c) Test at the 5% level of significance whether there is a difference between the mean fuel consumption of the two models of car. State your hypotheses and conclusion clearly.

(d) State any further assumption you made in order to be able to carry out your test in (c).

(e) Give two precautions which could be taken when undertaking an investigation into the fuel consumption of two models of car to ensure that a fair comparison is made. [E]

22 In an effort to increase the profit on the sale of his pigs a farmer decides to compare two brands, M and V, of pig feed. One of his sows has recently given birth to 13 piglets and so he assigns, at random, 8 to be fed on feed M and 5 on feed V.

Summarised below are the results obtained by the farmer, where x and y represent the weight, in kg, of the pigs fed on M and V respectively the day they were all sold.

$$\text{Feed } M: \sum x = 641.2, \ \sum x^2 = 51\,424.80$$

$$\text{Feed } V: \sum y = 409.9, \ \sum y^2 = 33\,626.32$$

Assuming that the weights of the piglets are normally distributed, test whether or not
(a) there is a difference between the variances,
(b) there is a difference between the means.   [E]

23 A hospital department installed a new, more sophisticated piece of equipment to replace an ageing one in the hope that it would speed up the treatment of patients. The treatment times of random samples of patients during the last week of operation of the old equipment and during the first week of operation of the new equipment were recorded. The summary results, in minutes, were:

	n	$\sum x$	$\sum x^2$
Old equipment	10	225	5136.3
New equipment	9	234	6200.0

(a) Show that the values of s^2 for the old and new equipment are 8.2 and 14.5 respectively.
Stating clearly your hypotheses, test
(b) whether the variance of the times using the new equipment is greater than the variance of the times using the old equipment, using a 5% significance level,
(c) whether there is a difference between the mean times for treatment using the new equipment and the old equipment, using a 2% significance level.
(d) Find 95% confidence limits for the mean difference in treatment times between the new and old equipment.
Even if the new equipment would eventually lead to a reduction in treatment times, to begin with treatment times using the new equipment might be higher than those using the old equipment.
(e) Give one reason why this might be so.

(f) Suggest how the comparison between the old and new equipment could be improved. [E]

24 Two ambulance stations, Greenwark and Derdeke, are in similar locations. Random samples of the response times, in minutes, to emergency calls were recorded during a particular week. The information is given in the table below:

Greenwark	22	11	12	13	14	12	31	17	15
Derdeke	12	6	7	5	4	3	19		

Stating your hypotheses clearly,

(a) test, at the 10% level of significance, whether or not the variances of the response times are the same,

(b) test, at the 5% level of significance, whether or not ambulances from Greenwark take longer on average to respond to emergency calls than ambulances from Derdeke. State an assumption you have made about the distributions of the response times.

(c) Explain why your result to part (a) enables you to carry out the test in part (b).

(d) Give a factor which has not been taken into account in your analysis. [E]

Examination style paper

S4

1. A machine fills '1 kg' packets of sugar. You may assume that the actual weight of sugar is normally distributed. The manufacturer requires the mean weight μ of sugar in the packets to be 1010 g with a variance of 9.
   The weights, in grams, of sugar in a sample of 7 packets taken at random from the machine were as follows:

   > 1012.9, 1018.1, 1015.6, 1021.3, 1006.0, 1010.2, 1011.8

   The mean of the packets was found to be within acceptable limits, but the manufacturer was concerned that the variance might have increased.
   (a) Calculate an unbiased estimate for the variance. **(3 marks)**
   (b) Test, at the 5% significance level, whether or not there is evidence to suggest that the variance has increased. **(4 marks)**

2. Coffee granules are sold in jars. The manufacturer claims that the weight of the coffee granules in the jars is normally distributed with a mean of 100 g.
   A sample of 20 jars is taken and the weight w of coffee granules in each jar carefully measured. The results are summarised by the following statistics:

   $$\sum w = 1968, \quad \sum w^2 = 193\,669$$

   Stating your hypotheses clearly, test at the 5% significance level whether or not there is evidence that the mean weight of coffee granules in the jars is less than that claimed by the manufacturer.
   (8 marks)

3. A candidate for mayor of a city is anxious to know the proportion p of the number of people who are likely to vote for him.
   Two separate polling organisations have done polls to find out the voter's intentions. The first organisation reports that out of m people surveyed X intended to vote for him, and the second that out of n were Y people.

   Possible estimators for p are $Q = \dfrac{1}{2}\left(\dfrac{X}{m} + \dfrac{Y}{n}\right)$ and $R = \dfrac{X+Y}{m+n}$.

   (a) Show that both are unbiased estimators of p. **(3 marks)**
   (b) Find $\operatorname{Var}(Q)$ and $\operatorname{Var}(R)$. **(3 marks)**
   Given that $X = 60$, $m = 200$, $Y = 82$ and $n = 300$,
   (c) State which of the two is the best estimator of p. **(2 marks)**

4. The following data gives the gains in weight, in kg, of 9 babies between birth and their first birthday:

   5.0, 7.2, 8.1, 9.3, 6.4, 7.8, 10.0, 8.1, and 6.3

   Assuming that in the population weight gains are normally distributed, find 95% confidence intervals for
   (a) the mean gain in weight of babies during their first year,
   (6 marks)
   (b) the variance of the weight gain. **(5 marks)**

5. Two training courses, Alpha and Beta, are designed to reduce the time taken to perform a certain task. In an experiment 14 workers are placed in pairs according to ability. One member of each pair is randomly allocated to Alpha and the other to Beta. The times taken, in seconds, for each worker to perform the task after the training course were recorded as given in the table below:

	Workers						
	1	2	3	4	5	6	7
Alpha	23.1	27.3	24.9	25.2	27.9	21.6	30.1
Beta	21.4	28.2	24.8	22.3	22.3	25.4	24.9

   Stating clearly your hypotheses and any assumption you make, use a paired t-test to determine, at the 5% significance level, whether or not the two courses are of equal effectiveness. [E] **(10 marks)**

6. A gambler tests a die for bias by throwing it 12 times, and he rejects it if there are 2 or fewer odd numbers in the sequence of throws.
   (a) Find the size of this test. **(1 mark)**
   (b) Explain why the power of this test is given by

   $$(1 - p)^{12} + 12p(1 - p)^{11} + 66p^2(1 - p)^{10}$$

   where p is the probability of getting an odd number. **(3 marks)**
   The table below gives values of the power for different values of p to two decimal places:

p	0.1	0.2	0.3	0.4	0.5
Power	0.89	r	0.25	s	0.02

   (c) Find values for r and s. **(2 marks)**
   (d) Using graph paper, draw a graph of the power function.
   (3 marks)
   (e) Find the range of values of p for which the probability of accepting the die as unbiased when it is biased is $\leqslant 0.4$. **(3 marks)**

7. Transport engineers have undertaken research into the strength of two different types of crash barrier, A and B, which are to be used on motorways. Independent random samples were taken from each

of the two types of crash barrier and the force needed to make each barrier buckle was recorded. The results (in kN) are given below:

Type A	3.1	4.2	3.7	6.1	5.3	4.9	
Type B	3.0	6.2	3.3	4.2	3.9	6.6	5.7

Given that $\sum x_A = 27.3$ and $\sum x_B = 32.9$,

(a) stating clearly any assumption you make, test at the 10% significance level whether the strengths of the two types of crash barrier have the same variance. **(9 marks)**

(b) Test at the 1% significance level whether the mean strengths of the two types of crash barrier are the same. State your hypotheses clearly. **(8 marks)**

(c) Explain why your answer to part (a) enables you to carry out the test in part (b). [E] **(2 marks)**

Appendix

Table 1 Binomial cumulative distribution function

The tabulated value is $P(X \leqslant x)$, where X has a binomial distribution with index n and parameter p.

$p =$	0.05	0.10	0.15	0.20	0.25	0.30	0.35	0.40	0.45	0.50
$n = 5, x = 0$	0.7738	0.5905	0.4437	0.3277	0.2373	0.1681	0.1160	0.0778	0.0503	0.0312
1	0.9774	0.9185	0.8352	0.7373	0.6328	0.5282	0.4284	0.3370	0.2562	0.1875
2	0.9988	0.9914	0.9734	0.9421	0.8965	0.8369	0.7648	0.6826	0.5931	0.5000
3	1.0000	0.9995	0.9978	0.9933	0.9844	0.9692	0.9460	0.9130	0.8688	0.8125
4	1.0000	1.0000	0.9999	0.9997	0.9990	0.9976	0.9947	0.9898	0.9815	0.9688
$n = 6, x = 0$	0.7351	0.5314	0.3771	0.2621	0.1780	0.1176	0.0754	0.0467	0.0277	0.0156
1	0.9672	0.8857	0.7765	0.6554	0.5339	0.4202	0.3191	0.2333	0.1636	0.1094
2	0.9978	0.9842	0.9527	0.9011	0.8306	0.7443	0.6471	0.5443	0.4415	0.3438
3	0.9999	0.9987	0.9941	0.9830	0.9624	0.9295	0.8826	0.8208	0.7447	0.6563
4	1.0000	0.9999	0.9996	0.9984	0.9954	0.9891	0.9777	0.9590	0.9308	0.8906
5	1.0000	1.0000	1.0000	0.9999	0.9998	0.9993	0.9982	0.9959	0.9917	0.9844
$n = 7, x = 0$	0.6983	0.4783	0.3206	0.2907	0.1335	0.0824	0.0490	0.0280	0.0152	0.0078
1	0.9556	0.8503	0.7166	0.5767	0.4449	0.3294	0.2338	0.1586	0.1024	0.0625
2	0.9962	0.9743	0.9262	0.8520	0.7564	0.6471	0.5323	0.4199	0.3164	0.2266
3	0.9998	0.9973	0.9879	0.9667	0.9294	0.8740	0.8002	0.7102	0.6083	0.5000
4	1.0000	0.9998	0.9988	0.9953	0.9871	0.9712	0.9444	0.9037	0.8471	0.7734
5	1.0000	1.0000	0.9999	0.9996	0.9987	0.9962	0.9910	0.9812	0.9643	0.9375
6	1.0000	1.0000	1.0000	1.0000	0.9999	0.9998	0.9994	0.9984	0.9963	0.9922
$n = 8, x = 0$	0.6634	0.4305	0.2725	0.1678	0.1001	0.0576	0.0319	0.0168	0.0084	0.0039
1	0.9428	0.8131	0.6572	0.5033	0.3671	0.2553	0.1691	0.1064	0.0632	0.0352
2	0.9942	0.9619	0.8948	0.7969	0.6785	0.5518	0.4278	0.3154	0.2201	0.1445
3	0.9996	0.9950	0.9786	0.9437	0.8862	0.8059	0.7064	0.5941	0.4770	0.3633
4	1.0000	0.9996	0.9971	0.9896	0.9727	0.9420	0.8939	0.8263	0.7396	0.6367
5	1.0000	1.0000	0.9998	0.9988	0.9958	0.9887	0.9747	0.9502	0.9115	0.8555
6	1.0000	1.0000	1.0000	0.9999	0.9996	0.9987	0.9964	0.9815	0.9819	0.9648
7	1.0000	1.0000	1.0000	1.0000	1.0000	0.9999	0.9998	0.9993	0.9983	0.9961
$n = 9, x = 0$	0.6302	0.3874	0.2316	0.1342	0.0751	0.0404	0.0207	0.0101	0.0046	0.0020
1	0.9288	0.7748	0.5995	0.4362	0.3003	0.1960	0.1211	0.0705	0.0385	0.0195
2	0.9916	0.9470	0.8591	0.7382	0.6007	0.4628	0.3373	0.2318	0.1495	0.0898
3	0.9994	0.9917	0.9661	0.9144	0.8343	0.7297	0.6089	0.4826	0.3614	0.2539
4	1.0000	0.9991	0.9944	0.9804	0.9511	0.9012	0.8283	0.7334	0.6214	0.5000
5	1.0000	0.9999	0.9994	0.9969	0.9900	0.9747	0.9464	0.9006	0.8342	0.7461
6	1.0000	1.0000	1.0000	0.9997	0.9987	0.9957	0.9888	0.9750	0.9502	0.9102
7	1.0000	1.0000	1.0000	1.0000	0.9999	0.9996	0.9986	0.9962	0.9909	0.9805
8	1.0000	1.0000	1.0000	1.0000	1.0000	1.0000	0.9999	0.9997	0.9992	0.9980

Table 1 — *continued*

p =	0.05	0.10	0.15	0.20	0.25	0.30	0.35	0.40	0.45	0.50
n = 10, x = 0	0.5987	0.3487	0.1969	0.1074	0.0563	0.0282	0.0135	0.0060	0.0025	0.0010
1	0.9139	0.7361	0.5443	0.3758	0.2440	0.1493	0.0860	0.0464	0.0233	0.0107
2	0.9885	0.9298	0.8202	0.6778	0.5256	0.3828	0.2616	0.1673	0.0996	0.0547
3	0.9990	0.9872	0.9500	0.8791	0.7759	0.6496	0.5138	0.3823	0.2660	0.1719
4	0.9999	0.9984	0.9901	0.9672	0.9219	0.8497	0.7515	0.6331	0.5044	0.3770
5	1.0000	0.9999	0.9986	0.9936	0.9803	0.9527	0.9051	0.8338	0.7384	0.6230
6	1.0000	1.0000	0.9999	0.9991	0.9965	0.9894	0.9740	0.9452	0.8980	0.8281
7	1.0000	1.0000	1.0000	0.9999	0.9996	0.9984	0.9952	0.9877	0.9726	0.9453
8	1.0000	1.0000	1.0000	1.0000	1.0000	0.9999	0.9995	0.9983	0.9955	0.9893
9	1.0000	1.0000	1.0000	1.0000	1.0000	1.0000	1.0000	0.9999	0.9997	0.9990
n = 12, x = 0	0.5404	0.2824	0.1422	0.0687	0.0317	0.0138	0.0057	0.0022	0.0008	0.0002
1	0.8816	0.6590	0.4435	0.2749	0.1584	0.0850	0.0424	0.0196	0.0083	0.0032
2	0.9804	0.8891	0.7358	0.5583	0.3907	0.2528	0.1513	0.0834	0.0421	0.0193
3	0.9978	0.9744	0.9078	0.7946	0.6488	0.4925	0.3467	0.2253	0.1345	0.0730
4	0.9998	0.9957	0.9761	0.9274	0.8424	0.7237	0.5833	0.4382	0.3044	0.1938
5	1.0000	0.9995	0.9954	0.9806	0.9456	0.8822	0.7873	0.6652	0.5269	0.3872
6	1.0000	0.9999	0.9993	0.9961	0.9857	0.9614	0.9154	0.8418	0.7393	0.6128
7	1.0000	1.0000	0.9999	0.9994	0.9972	0.9905	0.9745	0.9427	0.8883	0.8062
8	1.0000	1.0000	1.0000	0.9999	0.9996	0.9983	0.9944	0.9847	0.9644	0.9270
9	1.0000	1.0000	1.0000	1.0000	1.0000	0.9998	0.9992	0.9972	0.9921	0.9807
10	1.0000	1.0000	1.0000	1.0000	1.0000	1.0000	0.9999	0.9997	0.9989	0.9968
11	1.0000	1.0000	1.0000	1.0000	1.0000	1.0000	1.0000	1.0000	0.9999	0.9998
n = 15, x = 0	0.4633	0.2059	0.0874	0.0352	0.0134	0.0047	0.0016	0.0005	0.0001	0.0000
1	0.8290	0.5490	0.3186	0.1671	0.0802	0.0353	0.0142	0.0052	0.0017	0.0005
2	0.9638	0.8159	0.6042	0.3980	0.2361	0.1268	0.0617	0.0271	0.0107	0.0037
3	0.9945	0.9444	0.8227	0.6482	0.4613	0.2669	0.1727	0.0905	0.0424	0.0176
4	0.9994	0.9873	0.9383	0.8358	0.6865	0.5155	0.3519	0.2173	0.1204	0.0592
5	0.9999	0.9978	0.9832	0.9389	0.8516	0.7216	0.5643	0.4032	0.2608	0.1509
6	1.0000	0.9997	0.9964	0.9819	0.9434	0.8689	0.7548	0.6098	0.4522	0.3036
7	1.0000	1.0000	0.9994	0.9958	0.9827	0.9500	0.8868	0.7869	0.6536	0.5000
8	1.0000	1.0000	0.9999	0.9992	0.9958	0.9848	0.9578	0.9050	0.8182	0.6964
9	1.0000	1.0000	1.0000	0.9999	0.9992	0.9963	0.9876	0.9662	0.9231	0.8491
10	1.0000	1.0000	1.0000	1.0000	0.9999	0.9993	0.9972	0.9907	0.9745	0.9408
11	1.0000	1.0000	1.0000	1.0000	1.0000	0.9999	0.9995	0.9981	0.9937	0.9824
12	1.0000	1.0000	1.0000	1.0000	1.0000	1.0000	0.9999	0.9997	0.9989	0.9963
13	1.0000	1.0000	1.0000	1.0000	1.0000	1.0000	1.0000	1.0000	0.9999	0.9995
14	1.0000	1.0000	1.0000	1.0000	1.0000	1.0000	1.0000	1.0000	1.0000	1.0000
n = 20, x = 0	0.3585	0.1216	0.0388	0.0115	0.0032	0.0008	0.0002	0.0000	0.0000	0.0000
1	0.7358	0.3917	0.1756	0.0692	0.0243	0.0076	0.0021	0.0005	0.0001	0.0000
2	0.9245	0.6769	0.4049	0.2061	0.0913	0.0355	0.0121	0.0036	0.0009	0.0002
3	0.9841	0.8670	0.6477	0.4114	0.2252	0.1071	0.0444	0.0160	0.0049	0.0013
4	0.9974	0.9568	0.8298	0.6296	0.4148	0.2375	0.1182	0.0510	0.0189	0.0059
5	0.9997	0.9887	0.9327	0.8042	0.6172	0.4164	0.2454	0.1256	0.0553	0.0207
6	1.0000	0.9976	0.9781	0.9133	0.7858	0.6080	0.4166	0.2500	0.1299	0.0577
7	1.0000	0.9996	0.9941	0.9679	0.8982	0.7723	0.6010	0.4159	0.2520	0.1316
8	1.0000	0.9999	0.9987	0.9900	0.9591	0.8867	0.7624	0.5956	0.4143	0.2517
9	1.0000	1.0000	0.9998	0.9974	0.9861	0.9520	0.8782	0.7553	0.5914	0.4119
10	1.0000	1.0000	1.0000	0.9994	0.9961	0.9829	0.9468	0.8725	0.7507	0.5881
11	1.0000	1.0000	1.0000	0.9999	0.9991	0.9949	0.9804	0.9435	0.8692	0.7483
12	1.0000	1.0000	1.0000	1.0000	0.9998	0.9987	0.9940	0.9790	0.9420	0.8684
13	1.0000	1.0000	1.0000	1.0000	1.0000	0.9997	0.9985	0.9935	0.9786	0.9423
14	1.0000	1.0000	1.0000	1.0000	1.0000	1.0000	0.9997	0.9984	0.9936	0.9793
15	1.0000	1.0000	1.0000	1.0000	1.0000	1.0000	1.0000	0.9997	0.9985	0.9941
16	1.0000	1.0000	1.0000	1.0000	1.0000	1.0000	1.0000	1.0000	0.9997	0.9987
17	1.0000	1.0000	1.0000	1.0000	1.0000	1.0000	1.0000	1.0000	1.0000	0.9998
18	1.0000	1.0000	1.0000	1.0000	1.0000	1.0000	1.0000	1.0000	1.0000	1.0000

Table 1 — *continued*

p =	0.05	0.10	0.15	0.20	0.25	0.30	0.35	0.40	0.45	0.50
n = 25, x = 0	0.2774	0.0718	0.0172	0.0038	0.0008	0.0001	0.0000	0.0000	0.0000	0.0000
1	0.6424	0.2712	0.0931	0.0274	0.0070	0.0016	0.0003	0.0001	0.0000	0.0000
2	0.8729	0.5371	0.2537	0.0982	0.0321	0.0090	0.0021	0.0004	0.0001	0.0000
3	0.9659	0.7636	0.4711	0.2340	0.0962	0.0332	0.0097	0.0024	0.0005	0.0001
4	0.9928	0.9020	0.6821	0.4207	0.2137	0.0905	0.0320	0.0095	0.0023	0.0005
5	0.9988	0.9666	0.8385	0.6167	0.3783	0.1935	0.0826	0.0294	0.0086	0.0020
6	0.9998	0.9905	0.9305	0.7800	0.5611	0.3407	0.1734	0.0736	0.0258	0.0073
7	1.0000	0.9977	0.9745	0.8909	0.7265	0.5118	0.3061	0.1536	0.0639	0.0216
8	1.0000	0.9995	0.9920	0.9532	0.8506	0.6769	0.4668	0.2735	0.1340	0.0539
9	1.0000	0.9999	0.9979	0.9827	0.9287	0.8106	0.6303	0.4246	0.2424	0.1148
10	1.0000	1.0000	0.9995	0.9944	0.9703	0.9022	0.7712	0.5858	0.3843	0.2122
11	1.0000	1.0000	0.9999	0.9985	0.9893	0.9558	0.8746	0.7323	0.5426	0.3450
12	1.0000	1.0000	1.0000	0.9996	0.9966	0.9825	0.9396	0.8462	0.6937	0.5000
13	1.0000	1.0000	1.0000	0.9999	0.9991	0.9940	0.9745	0.9222	0.8173	0.6550
14	1.0000	1.0000	1.0000	1.0000	0.9998	0.9982	0.9907	0.9656	0.9040	0.7878
15	1.0000	1.0000	1.0000	1.0000	1.0000	0.9995	0.9971	0.9868	0.9560	0.8852
16	1.0000	1.0000	1.0000	1.0000	1.0000	0.9999	0.9992	0.9957	0.9826	0.9461
17	1.0000	1.0000	1.0000	1.0000	1.0000	1.0000	0.9998	0.9988	0.9942	0.9784
18	1.0000	1.0000	1.0000	1.0000	1.0000	1.0000	1.0000	0.9997	0.9984	0.9927
19	1.0000	1.0000	1.0000	1.0000	1.0000	1.0000	1.0000	0.9999	0.9996	0.9980
20	1.0000	1.0000	1.0000	1.0000	1.0000	1.0000	1.0000	1.0000	0.9999	0.9995
21	1.0000	1.0000	1.0000	1.0000	1.0000	1.0000	1.0000	1.0000	1.0000	0.9999
22	1.0000	1.0000	1.0000	1.0000	1.0000	1.0000	1.0000	1.0000	1.0000	1.0000
n = 30, x = 0	0.2146	0.0424	0.0076	0.0012	0.0002	0.0000	0.0000	0.0000	0.0000	0.0000
1	0.5535	0.1837	0.0480	0.0105	0.0020	0.0003	0.0000	0.0000	0.0000	0.0000
2	0.8122	0.4114	0.1514	0.0442	0.0106	0.0021	0.0003	0.0000	0.0000	0.0000
3	0.9392	0.6474	0.3217	0.1227	0.0374	0.0093	0.0019	0.0003	0.0000	0.0000
4	0.9844	0.8245	0.5245	0.2552	0.0979	0.0302	0.0075	0.0015	0.0002	0.0000
5	0.9967	0.9268	0.7106	0.4275	0.2026	0.0766	0.0233	0.0057	0.0011	0.0002
6	0.9994	0.9742	0.8474	0.6070	0.3481	0.1595	0.0586	0.0172	0.0040	0.0007
7	0.9999	0.9922	0.9302	0.7608	0.5143	0.2814	0.1238	0.0435	0.0121	0.0026
8	1.0000	0.9980	0.9722	0.8713	0.6736	0.4315	0.2247	0.0940	0.0312	0.0081
9	1.0000	0.9995	0.9903	0.9389	0.8034	0.5888	0.3575	0.1763	0.0694	0.0214
10	1.0000	0.9999	0.9971	0.9744	0.8943	0.7304	0.5078	0.2915	0.1350	0.0494
11	1.0000	1.0000	0.9992	0.9905	0.9493	0.8407	0.6548	0.4311	0.2327	0.1002
12	1.0000	1.0000	0.9998	0.9969	0.9784	0.9155	0.7802	0.5785	0.3592	0.1808
13	1.0000	1.0000	1.0000	0.9991	0.9918	0.9599	0.8737	0.7145	0.5025	0.2923
14	1.0000	1.0000	1.0000	0.9998	0.9973	0.9831	0.9348	0.8246	0.6448	0.4278
15	1.0000	1.0000	1.0000	0.9999	0.9992	0.9936	0.9699	0.9029	0.7691	0.5722
16	1.0000	1.0000	1.0000	1.0000	0.9998	0.9979	0.9876	0.9519	0.8644	0.7077
17	1.0000	1.0000	1.0000	1.0000	0.9999	0.9994	0.9955	0.9788	0.9286	0.8192
18	1.0000	1.0000	1.0000	1.0000	1.0000	0.9998	0.9986	0.9917	0.9666	0.8998
19	1.0000	1.0000	1.0000	1.0000	1.0000	1.0000	0.9996	0.9971	0.9862	0.9506
20	1.0000	1.0000	1.0000	1.0000	1.0000	1.0000	0.9999	0.9991	0.9950	0.9786
21	1.0000	1.0000	1.0000	1.0000	1.0000	1.0000	1.0000	0.9998	0.9984	0.9919
22	1.0000	1.0000	1.0000	1.0000	1.0000	1.0000	1.0000	1.0000	0.9996	0.9974
23	1.0000	1.0000	1.0000	1.0000	1.0000	1.0000	1.0000	1.0000	0.9999	0.9993
24	1.0000	1.0000	1.0000	1.0000	1.0000	1.0000	1.0000	1.0000	1.0000	0.9998
25	1.0000	1.0000	1.0000	1.0000	1.0000	1.0000	1.0000	1.0000	1.0000	1.0000

Table 1 — *continued*

p =	0.05	0.10	0.15	0.20	0.25	0.30	0.35	0.40	0.45	0.50
n = 40, x = 0	0.1285	0.0148	0.0015	0.0001	0.0000	0.0000	0.0000	0.0000	0.0000	0.0000
1	0.3991	0.0805	0.0121	0.0015	0.0001	0.0000	0.0000	0.0000	0.0000	0.0000
2	0.6767	0.2228	0.0486	0.0079	0.0010	0.0001	0.0000	0.0000	0.0000	0.0000
3	0.8619	0.4231	0.1302	0.0285	0.0047	0.0006	0.0001	0.0000	0.0000	0.0000
4	0.9520	0.6290	0.2633	0.0759	0.0160	0.0026	0.0003	0.0000	0.0000	0.0000
5	0.9861	0.7937	0.4325	0.1613	0.0433	0.0086	0.0013	0.0001	0.0000	0.0000
6	0.9966	0.9005	0.6067	0.2859	0.0962	0.0238	0.0044	0.0006	0.0001	0.0000
7	0.9993	0.9581	0.7559	0.4371	0.1820	0.0553	0.0124	0.0021	0.0002	0.0000
8	0.9999	0.9845	0.8646	0.5931	0.2998	0.1110	0.0303	0.0061	0.0009	0.0001
9	1.0000	0.9949	0.9328	0.7318	0.4395	0.1959	0.0644	0.0156	0.0027	0.0003
10	1.0000	0.9985	0.9701	0.8392	0.5839	0.3087	0.1215	0.0352	0.0074	0.0011
11	1.0000	0.9996	0.9880	0.9125	0.7151	0.4406	0.2053	0.0709	0.0179	0.0032
12	1.0000	0.9999	0.9957	0.9568	0.8209	0.5772	0.3143	0.1285	0.0386	0.0083
13	1.0000	1.0000	0.9986	0.9806	0.8968	0.7032	0.4408	0.2112	0.0751	0.0192
14	1.0000	1.0000	0.9996	0.9921	0.9456	0.8074	0.5721	0.3174	0.1326	0.0403
15	1.0000	1.0000	0.9999	0.9971	0.9738	0.8849	0.6946	0.4402	0.2142	0.0769
16	1.0000	1.0000	1.0000	0.9990	0.9884	0.9367	0.7978	0.5681	0.3185	0.1341
17	1.0000	1.0000	1.0000	0.9997	0.9953	0.9680	0.8761	0.6885	0.4391	0.2148
18	1.0000	1.0000	1.0000	0.9999	0.9983	0.9852	0.9301	0.7911	0.5651	0.3179
19	1.0000	1.0000	1.0000	1.0000	0.9994	0.9937	0.9637	0.8702	0.6844	0.4373
20	1.0000	1.0000	1.0000	1.0000	0.9998	0.9976	0.9827	0.9256	0.7870	0.5627
21	1.0000	1.0000	1.0000	1.0000	1.0000	0.9991	0.9925	0.9608	0.8669	0.6821
22	1.0000	1.0000	1.0000	1.0000	1.0000	0.9997	0.9970	0.9811	0.9233	0.7852
23	1.0000	1.0000	1.0000	1.0000	1.0000	0.9999	0.9989	0.9917	0.9595	0.8659
24	1.0000	1.0000	1.0000	1.0000	1.0000	1.0000	0.9996	0.9966	0.9804	0.9231
25	1.0000	1.0000	1.0000	1.0000	1.0000	1.0000	0.9999	0.9988	0.9914	0.9597
26	1.0000	1.0000	1.0000	1.0000	1.0000	1.0000	1.0000	0.9996	0.9966	0.9808
27	1.0000	1.0000	1.0000	1.0000	1.0000	1.0000	1.0000	0.9999	0.9988	0.9917
28	1.0000	1.0000	1.0000	1.0000	1.0000	1.0000	1.0000	1.0000	0.9996	0.9968
29	1.0000	1.0000	1.0000	1.0000	1.0000	1.0000	1.0000	1.0000	0.9999	0.9989
30	1.0000	1.0000	1.0000	1.0000	1.0000	1.0000	1.0000	1.0000	1.0000	0.9997
31	1.0000	1.0000	1.0000	1.0000	1.0000	1.0000	1.0000	1.0000	1.0000	0.9999
32	1.0000	1.0000	1.0000	1.0000	1.0000	1.0000	1.0000	1.0000	1.0000	1.0000

Table 1 — *continued*

$p =$	0.05	0.10	0.15	0.20	0.25	0.30	0.35	0.40	0.45	0.50
$n = 50, x = 0$	0.0769	0.0052	0.0003	0.0000	0.0000	0.0000	0.0000	0.0000	0.0000	0.0000
1	0.2794	0.0338	0.0029	0.0002	0.0000	0.0000	0.0000	0.0000	0.0000	0.0000
2	0.5405	0.1117	0.0142	0.0013	0.0001	0.0000	0.0000	0.0000	0.0000	0.0000
3	0.7604	0.2503	0.0460	0.0057	0.0005	0.0000	0.0000	0.0000	0.0000	0.0000
4	0.8964	0.4312	0.1121	0.0185	0.0021	0.0002	0.0000	0.0000	0.0000	0.0000
5	0.9622	0.6161	0.2194	0.0480	0.0070	0.0007	0.0001	0.0000	0.0000	0.0000
6	0.9882	0.7702	0.3613	0.1034	0.0194	0.0025	0.0002	0.0000	0.0000	0.0000
7	0.9968	0.8779	0.5188	0.1904	0.0453	0.0073	0.0008	0.0001	0.0000	0.0000
8	0.9992	0.9421	0.6681	0.3073	0.0916	0.0183	0.0025	0.0002	0.0000	0.0000
9	0.9998	0.9755	0.7911	0.4437	0.1637	0.0402	0.0067	0.0008	0.0001	0.0000
10	1.0000	0.9906	0.8801	0.5636	0.2622	0.0789	0.0160	0.0002	0.0002	0.0000
11	1.0000	0.9968	0.9372	0.7107	0.3816	0.1390	0.0342	0.0057	0.0006	0.0000
12	1.0000	0.9990	0.9699	0.8139	0.5110	0.2229	0.0661	0.0133	0.0018	0.0002
13	1.0000	0.9997	0.9868	0.8894	0.6370	0.3279	0.1163	0.0280	0.0045	0.0005
14	1.0000	0.9999	0.9947	0.9393	0.7481	0.4468	0.1878	0.0540	0.0104	0.0013
15	1.0000	1.0000	0.9981	0.9692	0.8369	0.5692	0.2801	0.0955	0.0220	0.0033
16	1.0000	1.0000	0.9993	0.9856	0.9017	0.6839	0.3889	0.1561	0.0427	0.0077
17	1.0000	1.0000	0.9998	0.9937	0.9449	0.7822	0.5060	0.2369	0.0765	0.0164
18	1.0000	1.0000	0.9999	0.9975	0.9713	0.8594	0.6216	0.3356	0.1273	0.0325
19	1.0000	1.0000	1.0000	0.9991	0.9861	0.9152	0.7264	0.4465	0.1974	0.0595
20	1.0000	1.0000	1.0000	0.9997	0.9937	0.9522	0.8139	0.5610	0.2862	0.1013
21	1.0000	1.0000	1.0000	0.9999	0.9974	0.9749	0.8813	0.6701	0.3900	0.1611
22	1.0000	1.0000	1.0000	1.0000	0.9990	0.9877	0.9290	0.7660	0.5019	0.2399
23	1.0000	1.0000	1.0000	1.0000	0.9996	0.9944	0.9604	0.8438	0.6134	0.3359
24	1.0000	1.0000	1.0000	1.0000	0.9999	0.9976	0.9793	0.9022	0.7160	0.4439
25	1.0000	1.0000	1.0000	1.0000	1.0000	0.9991	0.9900	0.9427	0.8034	0.5561
26	1.0000	1.0000	1.0000	1.0000	1.0000	0.9997	0.9955	0.9686	0.8721	0.6641
27	1.0000	1.0000	1.0000	1.0000	1.0000	0.9999	0.9981	0.9840	0.9220	0.7601
28	1.0000	1.0000	1.0000	1.0000	1.0000	1.0000	0.9993	0.9924	0.9556	0.8389
29	1.0000	1.0000	1.0000	1.0000	1.0000	1.0000	0.9997	0.9966	0.9765	0.8987
30	1.0000	1.0000	1.0000	1.0000	1.0000	1.0000	0.9999	0.9986	0.9884	0.9405
31	1.0000	1.0000	1.0000	1.0000	1.0000	1.0000	1.0000	0.9995	0.9947	0.9675
32	1.0000	1.0000	1.0000	1.0000	1.0000	1.0000	1.0000	0.9998	0.9978	0.9836
33	1.0000	1.0000	1.0000	1.0000	1.0000	1.0000	1.0000	0.9999	0.9991	0.9923
34	1.0000	1.0000	1.0000	1.0000	1.0000	1.0000	1.0000	1.0000	0.9997	0.9967
35	1.0000	1.0000	1.0000	1.0000	1.0000	1.0000	1.0000	1.0000	0.9999	0.9987
36	1.0000	1.0000	1.0000	1.0000	1.0000	1.0000	1.0000	1.0000	1.0000	0.9995
37	1.0000	1.0000	1.0000	1.0000	1.0000	1.0000	1.0000	1.0000	1.0000	0.9998
38	1.0000	1.0000	1.0000	1.0000	1.0000	1.0000	1.0000	1.0000	1.0000	1.0000

Table 2 Poisson cumulative distribution function

The tabulated value is $P(X \leqslant x)$, where X has a Poisson distribution with parameter λ.

$\lambda =$	0.5	1.0	1.5	2.0	2.5	3.0	3.5	4.0	4.5	5.0
$x = 0$	0.6065	0.3679	0.2231	0.1353	0.0821	0.0498	0.0302	0.0183	0.0111	0.0067
1	0.9098	0.7358	0.5578	0.4060	0.2873	0.1991	0.1359	0.0916	0.0611	0.0404
2	0.9856	0.9197	0.8088	0.6767	0.5438	0.4232	0.3208	0.2381	0.1736	0.1247
3	0.9982	0.9810	0.9344	0.8571	0.7576	0.6472	0.5366	0.4335	0.3423	0.2650
4	0.9998	0.9963	0.9814	0.9473	0.8912	0.8153	0.7254	0.6288	0.5321	0.4405
5	1.0000	0.9994	0.9955	0.9834	0.9580	0.9161	0.8576	0.7851	0.7029	0.6160
6	1.0000	0.9999	0.9991	0.9955	0.9858	0.9665	0.9347	0.8893	0.8311	0.7622
7	1.0000	1.0000	0.9998	0.9989	0.9958	0.9881	0.9733	0.9489	0.9134	0.8666
8	1.0000	1.0000	1.0000	0.9998	0.9989	0.9962	0.9901	0.9786	0.9597	0.9319
9	1.0000	1.0000	1.0000	1.0000	0.9997	0.9989	0.9967	0.9919	0.9829	0.9682
10	1.0000	1.0000	1.0000	1.0000	0.9999	0.9997	0.9990	0.9972	0.9933	0.9863
11	1.0000	1.0000	1.0000	1.0000	1.0000	0.9999	0.9997	0.9991	0.9976	0.9945
12	1.0000	1.0000	1.0000	1.0000	1.0000	1.0000	0.9999	0.9997	0.9992	0.9980
13	1.0000	1.0000	1.0000	1.0000	1.0000	1.0000	1.0000	0.9999	0.9997	0.9993
14	1.0000	1.0000	1.0000	1.0000	1.0000	1.0000	1.0000	1.0000	0.9999	0.9998
15	1.0000	1.0000	1.0000	1.0000	1.0000	1.0000	1.0000	1.0000	1.0000	0.9999
16	1.0000	1.0000	1.0000	1.0000	1.0000	1.0000	1.0000	1.0000	1.0000	1.0000
17	1.0000	1.0000	1.0000	1.0000	1.0000	1.0000	1.0000	1.0000	1.0000	1.0000
18	1.0000	1.0000	1.0000	1.0000	1.0000	1.0000	1.0000	1.0000	1.0000	1.0000
19	1.0000	1.0000	1.0000	1.0000	1.0000	1.0000	1.0000	1.0000	1.0000	1.0000

$\lambda =$	5.5	6.0	6.5	7.0	7.5	8.0	8.5	9.0	9.5	10.0
$x = 0$	0.0041	0.0025	0.0015	0.0009	0.0006	0.0003	0.0002	0.0001	0.0001	0.0000
1	0.0266	0.0174	0.0113	0.0073	0.0047	0.0030	0.0019	0.0012	0.0008	0.0005
2	0.0884	0.0620	0.0430	0.0296	0.0203	0.0138	0.0093	0.0062	0.0042	0.0028
3	0.2017	0.1512	0.1118	0.0818	0.0591	0.0424	0.0301	0.0212	0.0149	0.0103
4	0.3575	0.2851	0.2237	0.1730	0.1321	0.0996	0.0744	0.0550	0.0403	0.0293
5	0.5289	0.4457	0.3690	0.3007	0.2414	0.1912	0.1496	0.1157	0.0885	0.0671
6	0.6860	0.6063	0.5265	0.4497	0.3782	0.3134	0.2562	0.2068	0.1649	0.1301
7	0.8095	0.7440	0.6728	0.5987	0.5246	0.4530	0.3856	0.3239	0.2687	0.2202
8	0.8944	0.8472	0.7916	0.7291	0.6620	0.5925	0.5231	0.4557	0.3918	0.3328
9	0.9462	0.9161	0.8774	0.8305	0.7764	0.7166	0.6530	0.5874	0.5218	0.4579
10	0.9747	0.9574	0.9332	0.9015	0.8622	0.8159	0.7634	0.7060	0.6453	0.5830
11	0.9890	0.9799	0.9661	0.9467	0.9208	0.8881	0.8487	0.8030	0.7520	0.6968
12	0.9955	0.9912	0.9840	0.9730	0.9573	0.9362	0.9091	0.8758	0.8364	0.7916
13	0.9983	0.9964	0.9929	0.9872	0.9784	0.9658	0.9486	0.9261	0.8981	0.8645
14	0.9994	0.9986	0.9970	0.9943	0.9897	0.9827	0.9726	0.9585	0.9400	0.9165
15	0.9998	0.9995	0.9988	0.9976	0.9954	0.9918	0.9862	0.9780	0.9665	0.9513
16	0.9999	0.9998	0.9996	0.9990	0.9980	0.9963	0.9934	0.9889	0.9823	0.9730
17	1.0000	0.9999	0.9998	0.9996	0.9992	0.9984	0.9970	0.9947	0.9911	0.9857
18	1.0000	1.0000	0.9999	0.9999	0.9997	0.9993	0.9987	0.9976	0.9957	0.9928
19	1.0000	1.0000	1.0000	1.0000	0.9999	0.9997	0.9995	0.9989	0.9980	0.9965
20	1.0000	1.0000	1.0000	1.0000	1.0000	0.9999	0.9998	0.9996	0.9991	0.9984
21	1.0000	1.0000	1.0000	1.0000	1.0000	1.0000	0.9999	0.9998	0.9996	0.9993
22	1.0000	1.0000	1.0000	1.0000	1.0000	1.0000	1.0000	0.9999	0.9999	0.9997

Table 3 The normal distribution function

The function tabulated below is $\Phi(z)$, defined as

$$\Phi(z) = \frac{1}{\sqrt{2\pi}} \int_{\infty}^{z} e^{-\frac{1}{2}t^2}\, dt.$$

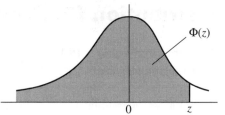

z	$\Phi(z)$	z	$\Phi(z)$	z	$\Phi(z)$	z	$\Phi(z)$	z	$\Phi(z)$
0.00	0.5000	0.50	0.6915	1.00	0.8413	1.50	0.9332	2.00	0.9772
0.01	0.5040	0.51	0.6950	1.01	0.8438	1.51	0.9345	2.02	0.9783
0.02	0.5080	0.52	0.6985	1.02	0.8461	1.52	0.9357	2.04	0.9793
0.03	0.5120	0.53	0.7019	1.03	0.8485	1.53	0.9370	2.06	0.9803
0.04	0.5160	0.54	0.7054	1.04	0.8508	1.54	0.9382	2.08	0.9812
0.05	0.5199	0.55	0.7088	1.05	0.8531	1.55	0.9394	2.10	0.9821
0.06	0.5239	0.56	0.7123	1.06	0.8554	1.56	0.9406	2.12	0.9830
0.07	0.5279	0.57	0.7157	1.07	0.8577	1.57	0.9418	2.14	0.9838
0.08	0.5319	0.58	0.7190	1.08	0.8599	1.58	0.9429	2.16	0.9846
0.09	0.5359	0.59	0.7224	1.09	0.8621	1.59	0.9441	2.18	0.9854
0.10	0.5398	0.60	0.7257	1.10	0.8643	1.60	0.9452	2.20	0.9861
0.11	0.5438	0.61	0.7291	1.11	0.8665	1.61	0.9463	2.22	0.9868
0.12	0.5478	0.62	0.7324	1.12	0.8686	1.62	0.9474	2.24	0.9875
0.13	0.5517	0.63	0.7357	1.13	0.8708	1.63	0.9484	2.26	0.9881
0.14	0.5557	0.64	0.7389	1.14	0.8729	1.64	0.9495	2.28	0.9887
0.15	0.5596	0.65	0.7422	1.15	0.8749	1.65	0.9505	2.30	0.9893
0.16	0.5636	0.66	0.7454	1.16	0.8770	1.66	0.9515	2.32	0.9898
0.17	0.5675	0.67	0.7486	1.17	0.8790	1.67	0.9525	2.34	0.9904
0.18	0.5714	0.68	0.7517	1.18	0.8810	1.68	0.9535	2.36	0.9909
0.19	0.5753	0.69	0.7549	1.19	0.8830	1.69	0.9545	2.38	0.9913
0.20	0.5793	0.70	0.7580	1.20	0.8849	1.70	0.9554	2.40	0.9918
0.21	0.5832	0.71	0.7611	1.21	0.8869	1.71	0.9564	2.42	0.9922
0.22	0.5871	0.72	0.7642	1.22	0.8888	1.72	0.9573	2.44	0.9927
0.23	0.5910	0.73	0.7673	1.23	0.8907	1.73	0.9582	2.46	0.9931
0.24	0.5948	0.74	0.7704	1.24	0.8925	1.74	0.9591	2.48	0.9934
0.25	0.5987	0.75	0.7734	1.25	0.8944	1.75	0.9599	2.50	0.9938
0.26	0.6026	0.76	0.7764	1.26	0.8962	1.76	0.9608	2.55	0.9946
0.27	0.6064	0.77	0.7794	1.27	0.8980	1.77	0.9616	2.60	0.9953
0.28	0.6103	0.78	0.7823	1.28	0.8997	1.78	0.9625	2.65	0.9960
0.29	0.6141	0.79	0.7852	1.29	0.9015	1.79	0.9633	2.70	0.9965
0.30	0.6179	0.80	0.7881	1.30	0.9032	1.80	0.9641	2.75	0.9970
0.31	0.6217	0.81	0.7910	1.31	0.9049	1.81	0.9649	2.80	0.9974
0.32	0.6255	0.82	0.7939	1.32	0.9066	1.82	0.9656	2.85	0.9978
0.33	0.6293	0.83	0.7967	1.33	0.9082	1.83	0.9664	2.90	0.9981
0.34	0.6331	0.84	0.7995	1.34	0.9099	1.84	0.9671	2.95	0.9984
0.35	0.6368	0.85	0.8023	1.35	0.9115	1.85	0.9678	3.00	0.9987
0.36	0.6406	0.86	0.8051	1.36	0.9131	1.86	0.9686	3.05	0.9989
0.37	0.6443	0.87	0.8078	1.37	0.9147	1.87	0.9693	3.10	0.9990
0.38	0.6480	0.88	0.8106	1.38	0.9162	1.88	0.9699	3.15	0.9992
0.39	0.6517	0.89	0.8133	1.39	0.9177	1.89	0.9706	3.20	0.9993
0.40	0.6554	0.90	0.8159	1.40	0.9192	1.90	0.9713	3.25	0.9994
0.41	0.6591	0.91	0.8186	1.41	0.9207	1.91	0.9719	3.30	0.9995
0.42	0.6628	0.92	0.8212	1.42	0.9222	1.92	0.9726	3.35	0.9996
0.43	0.6664	0.93	0.8238	1.43	0.9236	1.93	0.9732	3.40	0.9997
0.44	0.6700	0.94	0.8264	1.44	0.9251	1.94	0.9738	3.50	0.9998
0.45	0.6736	0.95	0.8289	1.45	0.9265	1.95	0.9744	3.60	0.9998
0.46	0.6772	0.96	0.8315	1.46	0.9279	1.96	0.9750	3.70	0.9999
0.47	0.6808	0.97	0.8340	1.47	0.9292	1.97	0.9756	3.80	0.9999
0.48	0.6844	0.98	0.8365	1.48	0.9306	1.98	0.9761	3.90	1.0000
0.49	0.6879	0.99	0.8389	1.49	0.9319	1.99	0.9767	4.00	1.0000
0.50	0.6915	1.00	0.8413	1.50	0.9332	2.00	0.9772		

Table 4 Percentage points of the normal distribution

The values z in the table are those which a random variable $Z \sim N(0, 1)$ exceeds with probability p, that is, $P(Z > z) = 1 - \Phi(z) = p$.

p	z	p	z
0.5000	0.0000	0.0500	1.6449
0.4000	0.2533	0.0250	1.9600
0.3000	0.5244	0.0100	2.3263
0.2000	0.8416	0.0050	2.5758
0.1500	1.0364	0.0010	3.0902
0.1000	1.2816	0.0005	3.2905

Table 5 Percentage points of the χ^2-distribution

The values in the table are those which a random variable with the χ^2-distribution on v degrees of freedom exceeds with the probability shown.

v	0.995	0.990	0.975	0.950	0.900	0.100	0.050	0.025	0.010	0.005
1	0.000	0.000	0.001	0.004	0.016	2.705	3.841	5.024	6.635	7.879
2	0.010	0.020	0.051	0.103	0.211	4.605	5.991	7.378	9.210	10.597
3	0.072	0.115	0.216	0.352	0.584	6.251	7.815	9.348	11.345	12.838
4	0.207	0.297	0.484	0.711	1.064	7.779	9.488	11.143	13.277	14.860
5	0.412	0.554	0.831	1.145	1.610	9.236	11.070	12.832	15.086	16.750
6	0.676	0.872	1.237	1.635	2.204	10.645	12.592	14.449	16.812	18.548
7	0.989	1.239	1.690	2.167	2.833	12.017	14.067	16.013	18.475	20.278
8	1.344	1.646	2.180	2.733	3.490	13.362	15.507	17.535	20.090	21.955
9	1.735	2.088	2.700	3.325	4.168	14.684	16.919	19.023	21.666	23.589
10	2.156	2.558	3.247	3.940	4.865	15.987	18.307	20.483	23.209	25.188
11	2.603	3.053	3.816	4.575	5.580	17.275	19.675	21.920	24.725	26.757
12	3.074	3.571	4.404	5.226	6.304	18.549	21.026	23.337	26.217	28.300
13	3.565	4.107	5.009	5.892	7.042	19.812	22.362	24.736	27.688	29.819
14	4.075	4.660	5.629	6.571	7.790	21.064	23.685	26.119	29.141	31.319
15	4.601	5.229	6.262	7.261	8.547	22.307	24.996	27.488	30.578	32.801
16	5.142	5.812	6.908	7.962	9.312	23.542	26.296	28.845	32.000	34.267
17	5.697	6.408	7.564	8.672	10.085	24.769	27.587	30.191	33.409	35.718
18	6.265	7.015	8.231	9.390	10.865	25.989	28.869	31.526	34.805	37.156
19	6.844	7.633	8.907	10.117	11.651	27.204	30.144	32.852	36.191	38.582
20	7.434	8.260	9.591	10.851	12.443	28.412	31.410	34.170	37.566	39.997
21	8.034	8.897	10.283	11.591	13.240	29.615	32.671	35.479	38.932	41.401
22	8.643	9.542	10.982	12.338	14.042	30.813	33.924	36.781	40.289	42.796
23	9.260	10.196	11.689	13.091	14.848	32.007	35.172	38.076	41.638	44.181
24	9.886	10.856	12.401	13.848	15.659	33.196	36.415	39.364	42.980	45.558
25	10.520	11.524	13.120	14.611	16.473	34.382	37.652	40.646	44.314	46.928
26	11.160	12.198	13.844	15.379	17.292	35.563	38.885	41.923	45.642	48.290
27	11.808	12.879	14.573	16.151	18.114	36.741	40.113	43.194	46.963	49.645
28	12.461	13.565	15.308	16.928	18.939	37.916	41.337	44.461	48.278	50.993
29	13.121	14.256	16.047	17.708	19.768	39.088	42.557	45.722	49.588	52.336
30	13.787	14.953	16.791	18.493	20.599	40.256	43.773	46.979	50.892	53.672

Table 6 Percentage points of Student's *t*-distribution

The values in the table are those which a random variable with Student's *t*-distribution on v degrees of freedom exceeds with the probability shown.

v	0.10	0.05	0.025	0.01	0.005	v	0.10	0.05	0.025	0.01	0.005
1	3.078	6.314	12.706	31.821	63.657	26	1.315	1.706	2.056	2.479	2.779
2	1.886	2.920	4.303	6.965	9.925	27	1.314	1.703	2.052	2.473	2.771
3	1.638	2.353	3.182	4.541	5.841	28	1.313	1.701	2.048	2.467	2.763
4	1.533	2.132	2.776	3.747	4.604	29	1.311	1.699	2.045	2.462	2.756
5	1.476	2.015	2.571	3.365	4.032	30	1.310	1.697	2.042	2.457	2.750
6	1.440	1.943	2.447	3.143	3.707	32	1.309	1.694	2.037	2.449	2.738
7	1.415	1.895	2.365	2.998	3.499	34	1.307	1.691	2.032	2.441	2.728
8	1.397	1.860	2.306	2.896	3.355	36	1.306	1.688	2.028	2.435	2.719
9	1.383	1.833	2.262	2.821	3.250	38	1.304	1.686	2.024	2.429	2.712
10	1.372	1.812	2.228	2.764	3.169	40	1.303	1.684	2.021	2.423	2.704
11	1.363	1.796	2.201	2.718	3.106	45	1.301	1.679	2.014	2.412	2.690
12	1.356	1.782	2.179	2.681	3.055	50	1.299	1.676	2.009	2.403	2.678
13	1.350	1.771	2.160	2.650	3.012	55	1.297	1.673	2.004	2.396	2.668
14	1.345	1.761	2.145	2.624	2.977	60	1.296	1.671	2.000	2.390	2.660
15	1.341	1.753	2.131	2.602	2.947	70	1.294	1.667	1.994	2.381	2.648
16	1.337	1.746	2.120	2.583	2.921	80	1.292	1.664	1.990	2.374	2.639
17	1.333	1.740	2.110	2.567	2.898	90	1.291	1.662	1.987	2.369	2.632
18	1.330	1.734	2.101	2.552	2.878	100	1.290	1.660	1.984	2.364	2.626
19	1.328	1.729	2.093	2.539	2.861	110	1.289	1.659	1.982	2.361	2.621
20	1.325	1.725	2.086	2.528	2.845	120	1.289	1.658	1.980	2.358	2.617
21	1.323	1.721	2.080	2.518	2.831						
22	1.321	1.717	2.074	2.508	2.819						
23	1.319	1.714	2.069	2.500	2.807						
24	1.318	1.711	2.064	2.492	2.797						
25	1.316	1.708	2.060	2.485	2.787						

Table 7 Percentage points of the *F*-distribution

The values in the table are those which a random variable with the *F*-distribution on v_1 and v_2 degrees of freedom exceeds with the probability 0.05 or 0.01.

Probability	v_2/v_1	1	2	3	4	5	6	8	10	12	24	∞
	1	161.4	199.5	215.7	224.6	230.2	234.0	238.9	241.9	243.9	249.1	254.3
	2	18.51	19.00	19.16	19.25	19.30	19.33	19.37	19.40	19.41	19.46	19.50
	3	10.13	9.55	9.28	9.12	9.01	8.94	8.85	8.79	8.74	8.64	8.53
	4	7.71	6.94	6.59	6.39	6.26	6.16	6.04	5.96	5.91	5.77	5.63
	5	6.61	5.79	5.41	5.19	5.05	4.95	4.82	4.74	4.68	4.53	4.37
	6	5.99	5.14	4.76	4.53	4.39	4.28	4.15	4.06	4.00	3.84	3.67
	7	5.59	4.74	4.35	4.12	3.97	3.87	3.73	3.64	3.57	3.41	3.23
	8	5.32	4.46	4.07	3.84	3.69	3.58	3.44	3.35	3.28	3.12	2.93
	9	5.12	4.26	3.86	3.63	3.48	3.37	3.23	3.14	3.07	2.90	2.71
	10	4.96	4.10	3.71	3.48	3.33	3.22	3.07	2.98	2.91	2.74	2.54
0.05	11	4.84	3.98	3.59	3.36	3.20	3.09	2.95	2.85	2.79	2.61	2.40
	12	4.75	3.89	3.49	3.26	3.11	3.00	2.85	2.75	2.69	2.51	2.30
	14	4.60	3.74	3.34	3.11	2.96	2.85	2.70	2.60	2.53	2.35	2.13
	16	4.49	3.63	3.24	3.01	2.85	2.74	2.59	2.49	2.42	2.24	2.01
	18	4.41	3.55	3.16	2.93	2.77	2.66	2.51	2.41	2.34	2.15	1.92
	20	4.35	3.49	3.10	2.87	2.71	2.60	2.45	2.35	2.28	2.08	1.84
	25	4.24	3.39	2.99	2.76	2.60	2.49	2.34	2.24	2.16	1.96	1.71
	30	4.17	3.32	2.92	2.69	2.53	2.42	2.27	2.16	2.09	1.89	1.62
	40	4.08	3.23	2.84	2.61	2.45	2.34	2.18	2.08	2.00	1.79	1.51
	60	4.00	3.15	2.76	2.53	2.37	2.25	2.10	1.99	1.92	1.70	1.39
	120	3.92	3.07	2.68	2.45	2.29	2.18	2.02	1.91	1.83	1.61	1.25
	∞	3.84	3.00	2.60	2.37	2.21	2.10	1.94	1.83	1.75	1.52	1.00
	1	4052.	5000.	5403.	5625.	5764.	5859.	5982.	6056.	6106.	6235.	6366.
	2	98.50	99.00	99.17	99.25	99.30	99.33	99.37	99.40	99.42	99.46	99.50
	3	34.12	30.82	29.46	28.71	28.24	27.91	27.49	27.23	27.05	26.60	26.13
	4	21.20	18.00	16.69	15.98	15.52	15.21	14.80	14.55	14.37	13.93	13.45
	5	16.26	13.27	12.06	11.39	10.97	10.67	10.29	10.05	9.89	9.47	9.02
	6	13.70	10.90	9.78	9.15	8.75	8.47	8.10	7.87	7.72	7.31	6.88
	7	12.20	9.55	8.45	7.85	7.46	7.19	6.84	6.62	6.47	6.07	5.65
	8	11.30	8.65	7.59	7.01	6.63	6.37	6.03	5.81	5.67	5.28	4.86
	9	10.60	8.02	6.99	6.42	6.06	5.80	5.47	5.26	5.11	4.73	4.31
	10	10.00	7.56	6.55	5.99	5.64	5.39	5.06	4.85	4.71	4.33	3.91
0.01	11	9.65	7.21	6.22	5.67	5.32	5.07	4.74	4.54	4.40	4.02	3.60
	12	9.33	6.93	5.95	5.41	5.06	4.82	4.50	4.30	4.16	3.78	3.36
	14	8.86	6.51	5.56	5.04	4.70	4.46	4.14	3.94	3.80	3.43	3.00
	16	8.53	6.23	5.29	4.77	4.44	4.20	3.89	3.69	3.55	3.18	2.75
	18	8.29	6.01	5.09	4.58	4.25	4.01	3.71	3.51	3.37	3.00	2.57
	20	8.10	5.85	4.94	4.43	4.10	3.87	3.56	3.37	3.23	2.86	2.42
	25	7.77	5.57	4.68	4.18	3.86	3.63	3.32	3.13	2.99	2.62	2.17
	30	7.56	5.39	4.51	4.02	3.70	3.47	3.17	2.98	2.84	2.47	2.01
	40	7.31	5.18	4.31	3.83	3.51	3.29	2.99	2.80	2.66	2.29	1.80
	60	7.08	4.98	4.13	3.65	3.34	3.12	2.82	2.63	2.50	2.12	1.60
	120	6.85	4.79	3.95	3.48	3.17	2.96	2.66	2.47	2.34	1.95	1.38
	∞	6.63	4.61	3.78	3.32	3.02	2.80	2.51	2.32	2.18	1.79	1.00

If an *upper* percentage point of the *F*-distribution on v_1 and v_2 degrees of freedom is *f*, then the corresponding *lower* percentage point of the *F* distribution on v_2 and v_1 degrees of freedom is $1/f$.

Answers

Exercise 1A

1 (a) $X \geqslant 51.5605$ (b) 0.01, 0.0162
2 (a) $X \leqslant 29.178$ (b) 0.05, 0.0869
3 (a) $X \geqslant 42.0606$ and $X \leqslant 37.9394$
  (b) 0.01, 0.5319
4 (a) $X \geqslant 6$ (b) 0.0197, 0.9527
5 (a) $X \leqslant 1$ (b) 0.0076, 0.9757
6 (a) $X \leqslant 1$ and $X \geqslant 9$
  (b) 0.0278, 0.9519
7 (a) $X \geqslant 11$ (b) 0.0426, 0.9015
8 (a) $X = 0$ (b) 0.0111, 0.9698
9 (a) $X \geqslant 16$ and $X \leqslant 3$
  (b) 0.0432. 0.9494
10 (a) $X \geqslant 15.392$ and $X \leqslant 14.608$
   (b) 0.1492
11 (a) $\bar{x} = 42.403$ (b) 0.6103
   (c) Increase type II error decrease type I therefore leave.

Exercise 1B

1 (a) $\bar{x} \geqslant 20.98694$ (b) 0.3783
2 (a) 0.0196   (b) 0.0051
3 (a) 0.0111   (b) 0.0166
4 0.3522
5 (a) 0.0430   (c) 0.68, 0.12
  (e) 2.65
6 (a) 0.0421   (c) 0.0028

Exercise 1C

1 (a) unbiased   (b) biased, $-\frac{\mu}{4}$
  (c) unbiased   (d) unbiased
  (e) biased, $\frac{\mu}{5}$

2 (a) $\frac{13}{32}\sigma^2$ (c) $\frac{5}{9}\sigma^2$ (d) $\frac{1}{3}\sigma^2$
  (d) is the most efficient since it has the smallest variance
3 (a) $\mathrm{E}(\bar{X}) = \mu$, $\mathrm{Var}(\bar{X}) = \dfrac{\sigma^2}{n}$

  (b) $\mathrm{E}(\bar{X}) = \mu$, $\mathrm{Var}(\bar{X}) = \dfrac{2}{3}\dfrac{(2n+1)}{n(n+1)}\sigma^2$

4 (a) (i) biased, $\frac{a}{2}$ (ii) unbiased
      (iii) biased, $3a$
  (b) (i) $\dfrac{a^2}{4}$ (ii) $\dfrac{a^2}{9}$ (iii) $2a^2$
  (c) use (ii), it is unbiased
  (d) $5\frac{2}{15}$
5 50
6 (a) $\mathrm{E}(\hat{p}_1) = p$ $\mathrm{Var}(\hat{p}_1) = \frac{25}{49}\dfrac{p(1-p)}{n}$

  $\mathrm{E}(\hat{p}_2) = p$ $\mathrm{Var}(\hat{p}_2) = \frac{1}{2}\dfrac{p(1-p)}{n}$
  (b) $\hat{p}_2$ has the least variance so is the best estimator
7 (a) $\mathrm{E}(X) = p$ $\mathrm{Var}(X) = p(1-p) = pq$
  (c) $\mathrm{Var}(X) = p(1-p)(a_1^2 + a_2^2 + a_3^2)$
  (d) (i) and (iii) are unbiased
  $\mathrm{Var}(\mathrm{i}) = \frac{9}{25}pq$, $\mathrm{Var}(\mathrm{iii}) = \frac{41}{81}pq$,
  (i) is the better estimator

Exercise 2A

1 (a) $t < -2.179$ (b) $t > 1.782$
  (c) $|t| > 2.179$
2 (a) 2.479   (b) 1.706
3 (a) 1.812   (b) -2.738 (c) -2.571
  (d) -2.583 and 2.583
  (e) -1.734 and 1.734

4 critical value 0.492

test statistic 2.132; not critical; no evidence that μ is not 11

5 critical value -2.473

test statistic -5.027; critical; evidence that μ is not 19

6 critical value ± 2.179

test statistic 1.172; not critical; no evidence that μ is not 3

7 $H_0 : \mu = 100$ $H_1 : \mu < 100$

critical value -1.761

test statistic -0.443; not critical; no evidence that μ is not 100

8 $H_0 : \mu = 1000$ $H_1 : \mu > 1000$

critical value 1.895

test statistic 1.448; not critical; no evidence that μ is not 1000

9 $H_0 : \mu = 6$ $H_1 : \mu > 6$

critical value 2.160

test statistic 1.967; not critical; no evidence supporting manufacturer's claim

10 $H_0 : \mu = 1.00$ $H_1 : \mu > 1.00$

critical value 1.328

test statistic 0.752; not critical; no evidence that μ is not 1.00

Exercise 2B

1 (18.624, 23.276)

2 (9.959, 14.841)

3 (a) (174.808, 183.859)

(b) (173.559, 185.108)

4 (9.706, 11.014)

5 (23.397, 31.628)

6 (115.94, 128.06)

Exercise 2C

1 (a) 3.6373

(b) $H_0 : \sigma^2 = 1.5$ $H_1 : \sigma^2 > 1.5$

critical value 30.144

test statistic 46.073; critical; there is evidence of a change in variance

2 critical value 2.7

test statistic 0.287; critical; there is evidence to suggest that variance is not 0.09

3 critical values 2.7 and 19.023

test statistic 15.235; not critical; there is no evidence of a change in variance

4 critical values 8.907 and 32.852

test statistic 17.419; not critical; there is no evidence of a change in variance

5 (a) 9.996, 0.0264

(b) (i) Critical values ± 2.145

test statistic -0.577; not critical; no evidence of a change in means

(ii) Critical values 5.629 and 26.119

Test statistic 0.244; critical; there is evidence that the variance is not 0.04

6 (a) 0.061 25

(b) 4.3125

critical values 1.895

test statistic 2.3143; critical; mean weight is not 4.11

(c) critical values 2.167 and 14.067

test statistic 2.26; not critical; do not reject H_0

7 (a) $H_0 : \sigma^2 = 110.25$ $H_1 : \sigma^2 < 110.25$

critical value 10.117

test statistic 12.451; not critical; there is no evidence that the variance has decreased

(b) take a larger sample before committing to new component

Exercise 2D

1 (2.573, 11.938)

2 (0.259, 0.722)

3 (0.241, 1.191)

4 (a) (6.348, 9.892)

(b) (0.731, 16.835)

5 (a) (i) (58.364, 65.836)

(ii) (22.099, 112.451)

6 (225.343, 250.657)

(148.136, 1043.704)

Review exercise 1

1 (a) $X \geqslant 9$ (b)   0.0422   (c)   0.3036

2 (a) $X = 0$ (b)   0.0302   (c)   0.0498

3 (a) (6.614, 9.386)   (b)   0.05
   (c)   0.7084   (d)   0.2916

4 (a) 0.0866   (b)   0.0511, 0.2560, 0.6761

5 (a) 0.0424   (b)   0.6482, 0.0905

6 (a) $\dfrac{1}{25}$ (b) $\dfrac{3m}{50}$

7 (b) $\dfrac{X + Y}{7}$

8 $H_0 : \mu = 28$ $H_1 : \mu > 28$
critical value 1.771
test statistic 1.4967; not critical; no evidence to
suggest that $\mu > 28$

9 critical value 1.895
test statistic 0.571; not critical; no evidence to
suggest that $\mu > 10$

10 (a) (54.641, 51.025)
   (b)   (1.156, 17.850)

11 (a) (9.452, 10.148)
   (b)   (0.276, 1.101)

12 (a) (0.946, 4.672)
   (b)   (1.046, 3.971)

13 (a) 0.0548
   (b)   0.8791
   (c)   Test more discriminating for higher
values

14 (a) H_0 rejected when true
   (b)   P(type I error)
   (c)   0.0571

15 (a) $H_0 : \mu = 2$ $H_1 : \mu > 2$
   (b) $X \geqslant 5$
   (c)   0.3712

16 $H_0 : \mu = 21.5$ $H_1 : \mu < 21.5$
critical value $t = -1.895$,
test statistic $t = -0.5817$; not significant; no
evidence to reject claim

17 (a) $H_0 : \lambda = 2, H_1 : \lambda > 2$ (b) $X \geqslant 5$
   (c)   0.1847   (d) $Y \geqslant 11$
   (e)   0.2940
   (f)   Test more powerful using 3 days

18 (a) 0.0620
   (c) $s = 0.6767, t = 0.1247$
   (e) $\mu < 1.55$

19 (a) (5.71, 6.67)   (b)   (0.535, 1.28)
   (c)   needs to measure at the same time each
day

20 (a) $E(X) = p$, $Var(X) = pq$
   (b) $a_1 + a_2 + a_3 = 1$
   (c) $(a_1 + a_2 + a_3) pq$
   (d)   (i)   is best, smallest variance

21 (b) $\dfrac{pq}{4} \left(\dfrac{n + m}{nm} \right), \dfrac{pq}{n + m}$
   (c) $\hat{p}_2$ since $Var(\hat{p}_2) < Var(\hat{p}_1)$

22 (a) (9.948, 36.69)   (b)   6.079
   (c) $\sqrt{36.690} < 6.079$

23 (a) 9.32 and 13.68   (b)   1.68 and 25.9

24 (a) τ_1 bias $= 0$, τ_2 bias $= \tau \left(1 - \dfrac{1}{\sqrt{3}} \right)$,
τ_3 bias $= 0$
   (b) $\dfrac{\tau^2}{6}, \dfrac{\tau^2}{6}, \dfrac{\tau^2}{8}$
   (c) τ_3 has least variance
   (d) τ_2 is worst because it is biased

25 (a) critical region $\chi^2 > 16.919$
test statistic $\chi^2 = 15.21$; no reason to reject H_0;
standard deviation $= 4$ months
   (b)   critical region $t > 1.833$
Test statistic $t = 1.946$; evidence to reject H_0;
mean battery life > 24
   (c)   lifetime is normally distributed

26 (a) (717, 726)
   (b)   (7.909, 15.189)
   (c)   725 within confidence interval, no
evidence to reject H_0

27 (a) Critical region $\chi^2 > 19.023$
Test statistic $\chi^2 = 16.836$; no evidence to reject
H_0
   (b)   Critical region $z > 1.6449$
Test statistic $z = 3.225$; reject H_0; evidence to
suggest there is an increase in breaking strain
   (c)   in (a) there was no change in σ so assume
$\sigma = 5$ $\therefore$ use z not t

28 (a) 0.0547   (c) 0.06152

(d) $(1-p)^5 + \{1-(1-p)^5\}(1-p)^5$

(e) 0.0256, 0.2616

(f) Text A since power test A > power test B

29 (a) 0.5151

(b) (i) (2.9066, 3.9334)

(ii) (0.4937, 1.3103)

(c) Confidence intervals for new method standard deviation suggest that it is quite variable. Although sample mean slightly less, confidence interval provides no evidence that it has decreased. Stay with old method.

(d) Use a paired design – each engineer uses both methods then compare.

30 (a) 2.4013, 2.9986

(c) $\bar{y} > 3.39$ (d) 0.6784

Exercise 3A

1 (a) 2.34   (b) 3.36   (c) 3.37

2 (a) 0.241   (b) 0.463   (c) 0.198

3 (a) 3.37   (b) 4.20   (c) 6.06

4 (a) 0.037   (b) 0.176   (c) 0.101

5 (a) 0.299, 3.07   (b) 0.364, 2.91

(c) 0.111, 0.111

6 0.05   **7** 0.90

Exercise 3B

1 critical region $f > 4.06$

test statistic 1.1875; not critical; accept H_0

2 critical region $f > 2.29$

test statistic 2.4706; critical; reject H_0

3 critical region $f > 4.82$

test statistic 1.144; not critical; accept H_0

4 critical region $f > 2.85$

test statistic 1.445; not critical; accept H_0

5 (a) critical region $f > 5.19$

test statistic 5.64; critical; reject H_0

(b) Hold tight cheaper, less variable

6 critical region $f > 10.97$

test statistic 9.336; not critical; accept H_0

7 (a) $\mu_1 = 1046$ $s_1^2 = 1818.11$ and $\mu_2 = 997.75$; $s_2^2 = 1200.21$

(b) critical region $f > 3.73$

test statistic 1.5148; not critical; accept H_0

(c) Use first supplier who appears to have a higher mean.

Exercise 3C

1 $s_p^2 = 12$, critical region $t > 2.045$

test statistic 1.538; not critical; do not reject H_0

2 $s_p^2 = 4.075$, critical region $t > 1.860$

test statistic 2.270; critical; reject H_0

3 (a) $s_p^2 = 0.000\,827$, critical region $t > 1.812$

test statistic 1.445; not critical; accept H_0

(b) $s_p^2 = 0.000\,78$, critical region $t > 1.746$

test statistic 7.706; critical; reject H_0

4 (a) $s_p = 2.189$, (1.151, 4.849)

(b) independent samples, normal distributions, common variance

5 (a) $s_p = 0.856$, critical region $t > 1.746$

test statistic 7.71; critical; reject H_0

(b) (2.419, 3.836)

Exercise 3D

1 (a) (i) $H_0: \mu = 0$, $H_1: \mu \neq 0$

(ii) $H_0: \mu = 0$, $H_1: \mu > 0$

(b) $\bar{d} = 5$, $s = 4.195$

critical region $t > 2.015$

test statistic 2.919; critical; reject H_0

2 $\bar{d} = 0.5$, $s = 2.506$

critical region $t > 2.821$

test statistic 0.631; not critical; accept H_0

3 $\bar{d} = 4.7$, $s = 3.234$

critical region $t > 1.833$

test statistic 4.596; critical; reject H_0; journeys are quicker

4 $\bar{d} = 4.6$, $s = 3.718$

critical region $t > 1.833$

test statistic 3.913; critical; reject H_0

5 (a) $\bar{d} = 2.5$, $s = 8.896$

critical region $t > 1.895$

test statistic 0.795; not critical; accept H_0

(b)   the differences are normally distributed

6   critical value 1.833

test statistic 5.095; critical; evidence to suggest a tea break increases the number of garments made

Review exercise 2

1   critical value 2.24

test statistic 1.147; not critical; no evidence to suggest $\sigma_1^2 > \sigma_2^2$

2   critical value 3.64

test statistic 1.304; not critical; no evidence to suggest $\sigma_1^2 > \sigma_2^2$. Have assumed populations are normally distributed.

3   Critical value 1.691

test statistic 1.837; not critical; no evidence to suggest mean has decreased

4   (a)   using same people eliminates changes due to other factors such as variability between people

(b)   critical value 1.761

test statistic 2.014; critical; evidence to suggest that reactions are slower in the evening

5   (a)   eliminates variability due to inheritance

(b)   critical value 1.812

test statistic 3.318; critical; evidence to uphold manufacturer's claim

6   critical value 1.895

test statistic 2.252; critical; evidence to suggest manufacturer's claim is justified

7   critical value 1.701

test statistic 0.544; not critical; no evidence to suggest that employees stay longer in the North

8   0.99

9   (b)   0.001 09

10   (a)   critical region $F > 3.28$

F ratio $= 3.57$; reject H_0; there is evidence that the machines differ in variability

(b)   population distributions assumed normal

11   critical region $F > 2.85$

test statistic $F = 3.3699$; significant; there is evidence to suggest that their variances differ

12 $H_0: \mu = 0.6$, $H_1: \mu > 0.6$

critical value $t_3 = 2.353$

test statistic $t_3 = 4.1025$; reject H_0; evidence to suggest the difference is too great

13   critical region $|t| > 2.262$

test statistic $t = 1.9392$; do not reject H_0; no difference in boards

14   critical region $t > 1.833$

test statistic $t = 3.7101$; reject H_0; evidence of mean loss of weight

15   (a)   (0.6392, 10.3608)

(b)   normality and equal variances

(c)   zero not in interval so method B seems better than method A

16 $H_0: \mu = 0.6$, $H_1: \mu > 0.6$

critical region $t > 2.998$

test statistic $t = 2.3686$; do not reject H_0; no evidence of a difference in means

17   (a) $H_0 : \mu_{old} = \mu_{new}$, $H_1 : \mu_{old} > \mu_{new}$

(b)   critical value $t_{14} = 1.761$

test statistic $t = 1.8446$; significant; there is evidence to suggest that new language does improve time

(c)   Once task is solved the programmer should be quicker next time with either language

18   (a)   critical region $t > 1.860$

test statistic $t = 1.596$, not critical; no significant improvement

(b)   normality

(c)   critical region $t > 1.397$; reject H_0

(d)   evidence strong enough to reject H_0 at 10% level but not at 5% level

19   (a)   normal is suspect because of high value

(b)   critical region $t > 1.833$

test statistic $t = 1.850$; reject H_0; there has been a decrease in daily consumption

(c)   assume same variances $(-0.149, 8.749)$

20   (a)   critical region $|t| > 2.042$

test statistic $t = -1.3181$; do not reject H_0; no difference in milk yield

(b)   independent samples, equal variances

(c)   Some goats in both, some different.

(d)   paired t test using only goats common to both

21 (b)   20.464

(c)   critical region $|t| > 2.060$

test statistic $t = 2.0547$, accept H_0; no evidence to suggest difference in means

(d)   normality

(e)   same types of driving, roads and weather

22 (a)   critical region $F > 4.12$

test statistic $F = 1.2187$; not significant; there is no evidence to suggest that their variances differ

(b)   critical region $t > 2.201$

test statistic $t = 1.4311$; do not reject H_0; no evidence of a difference in mean weights of each brand

23 (b)   critical region $F > 3.23$

test statistic $F = 1.768$; not critical; no change in variance

(c)   critical region $|t| > 2.567$

test statistic $t = 2.2798$; not critical; no difference in means

(d)   (0.261, 6.739)

(e)   need to learn new equipment

(f)   gather data on new equipment after it has been mastered

24 (a)   critical region $F > 4.15$

test statistic $F = 1.297$; not significant; there is no evidence to suggest that their variances differ

(b)   critical region $t > 1.761$

test statistic $t = 2.692$; reject H_0; response times for $G >$ than for D

(c)   needs equal variances for pooled variance

(d)   different drivers from same station

Examination style paper S4

1 (a)   26.087   (b) $H_0 : \sigma^2 = 9$ $H_1 : \sigma^2 > 9$

critical region > 12.592

test statistic 17.391; significant; variance has increased

2 $H_0 : \mu = 100$ $H_1 : \mu < 100$

critical region $t < -1.729$

test statistic -7.393

significant; sufficient evidence that $\mu < 100$

3 (b) $\mathrm{Var}(p_1) = \dfrac{p}{4}(1 - p)\left(\dfrac{1}{m} + \dfrac{1}{n}\right)$

$\mathrm{Var}(p_2) = p(1 - p)\dfrac{1}{(m + n)}$

(c) p_2 has lowest variance

4 (a)   (6.386, 8.770)

(b)   (1.097, 8.824)

5 $H_0 : \mu_d = 0$ $H_1 : \mu_d \neq 0$

$\bar{d} = 1.543$, critical region $|t| > 2.447$

test statistic 1.2099; not significant; there is evidence that the two courses are equally effective

6 (a)   0.0193

(c) $r = 0.56$, $s = 0.08$

(e) $p < 0.19$

7 (a)   Assume normality, $H_0 : \sigma_A^2 = \sigma_B^2$

$H_1 : \sigma_A^2 \neq \sigma_B^2$, critical region > 4.95

test statistic 1.7398; not significant; no evidence that variances are not the same

(b) $H_0 : \mu_A = \mu_B$, $H_1 : \mu_A \neq \mu_B$ $s_p^2 = 1.694$

critical region $|t| > 3.106$

test statistic -0.2071; not significant; no evidence of a difference in mean strengths

(c)   Pooled estimate of variance requires the variances to be the same, (a) suggests this is reasonable

List of symbols and notation

The following notation will be used in all Edexcel examinations.

$\in$	is an element of
$\notin$	is not an element of
$\{x_1, x_2, \ldots\}$	the set with elements $x_1, x_2, \ldots$
$\{x : \ldots\}$	the set of all x such that $\ldots$
$\mathrm{n}(A)$	the number of elements in set A
$\varnothing$	the empty set
$\mathscr{E}$	the universal set
A'	the complement of the set A
$\mathbb{N}$	the set of natural numbers, $\{1, 2, 3, \ldots\}$
$\mathbb{Z}$	the set of integers, $\{0, \pm 1, \pm 2, \pm 3, \ldots\}$
$\mathbb{Z}^+$	the set of positive integers, $\{1, 2, 3, \ldots\}$
$\mathbb{Z}_n$	the set of integers modulo n, $\{0, 1, 2, \ldots, n-1\}$
$\mathbb{Q}$	the set of rational numbers $\left\{\dfrac{p}{q} : p \in \mathbb{Z}, q \in \mathbb{Z}^+\right\}$
$\mathbb{Q}^+$	the set of positive rational numbers, $\{x \in \mathbb{Q} : x > 0\}$
$\mathbb{Q}_0^+$	the set of positive rational numbers and zero, $\{x \in \mathbb{Q} : x \geqslant 0\}$
$\mathbb{R}$	the set of real numbers
$\mathbb{R}^+$	the set of positive real numbers, $\{x \in \mathbb{R} : x > 0\}$
$\mathbb{R}_0^+$	the set of positive real numbers and zero, $\{x \in \mathbb{R} : x \geqslant 0\}$
$\mathbb{C}$	the set of complex numbers
(x, y)	the ordered pair x, y
$A \times B$	the cartesian product of sets A and B, $A \times B = \{(a, b) : a \in A, b \in B\}$
$\subseteq$	is a subset of
$\subset$	is a proper subset of
$\cup$	union
$\cap$	intersection
$[a, b]$	the closed interval, $\{x \in \mathbb{R} : a \leqslant x \leqslant b\}$
$[a, b), [a, b[$	the interval $\{x \in \mathbb{R} : a \leqslant x < b\}$
$(a, b],]a, b]$	the interval $\{x \in \mathbb{R} : a < x \leqslant b\}$
$(a, b),]a, b[$	the open interval $\{x \in \mathbb{R} : a < x < b\}$
$y\,R\,x$	y is related to x by the relation R
$y \sim x$	y is equivalent to x, in the context of some equivalence relation
$=$	is equal to
$\neq$	is not equal to
$\equiv$	is identical to *or* is congruent to

$\approx$	is approximately equal to
$\cong$	is isomorphic to
$\propto$	is proportional to
$<$	is less than
$\leqslant$, $\not>$	is less than or equal to, is not greater than
$>$	is greater than
$\geqslant$, $\not<$	is greater than or equal to, is not less than
∞	infinity
$p \wedge q$	p and q
$p \vee q$	p or q (or both)
$\sim p$	not p
$p \Rightarrow q$	p implies q (if p then q)
$p \Leftarrow q$	p is implied by q (if q then p)
$p \Leftrightarrow q$	p implies and is implied by q (p is equivalent to q)
$\exists$	there exists
$\forall$	for all
$a + b$	a plus b
$a - b$	a minus b
$a \times b$, ab, $a.b$	a multiplied by b
$a \div b$, $\dfrac{a}{b}$, a/b	a divided by b
$\displaystyle\sum_{i=1}^{n} a_i$	$a_1 + a_2 + \ldots + a_n$
$\displaystyle\prod_{i=1}^{n} a_i$	$a_1 \times a_2 \times \ldots \times a_n$
$\sqrt{a}$	the positive square root of a
$|a|$	the modulus of a
$n!$	n factorial
$\dbinom{n}{r}$	the binomial coefficient $\dfrac{n!}{r!(n-r)!}$ for $n \in \mathbb{Z}^+$ $\dfrac{n(n-1)\ldots(n-r+1)}{r!}$ for $n \in \mathbb{Q}$
$f(x)$	the value of the function f at x
$f: A \to B$	f is a function under which each element of set A has an image in set B
$f: x \mapsto y$	the function f maps the element x to the element y
f^{-1}	the inverse function of the function f
$g \circ f$, gf	the composite function of f and g which is defined by $(g \circ f)(x)$ or $gf(x) = g(f(x))$
$\displaystyle\lim_{x \to a} f(x)$	the limit of $f(x)$ as x tends to a
Δx, δx	an increment of x
$\dfrac{dy}{dx}$	the derivative of y with respect to x
$\dfrac{d^n y}{dx^n}$	the nth derivative of y with respect to x

$f'(x), f''(x), \ldots, f^{(n)}(x)$	the first, second, $\ldots$, nth derivatives of $f(x)$ with respect to x
$\int y \, dx$	the indefinite integral of y with respect to x
$\int_a^b y \, dx$	the definite integral of y with respect to x between the limits $x = a$ and $x = b$
$\dfrac{\partial V}{\partial x}$	the partial derivative of V with respect to x
$\dot{x}, \ddot{x}, \ldots$	the first, second, $\ldots$ derivatives of x with respect to t
e	base of natural logarithms
e^x, exp x	exponential function of x
$\log_a x$	logarithm to the base a of x
$\ln x$, $\log_e x$	natural logarithm of x
$\lg x$, $\log_{10} x$	logarithm of to base 10
sin, cos, tan cosec, sec, cot	the circular functions
arcsin, arccos, arctan arccosec, arcsec, arccot	the inverse circular functions
sinh, cosh, tanh cosech, sech, coth	the hyperbolic functions
arsinh, arcosh, artanh, arcosech, arsech, arcoth	the inverse hyperbolic functions
i, j	square root of -1
z	a complex number, $z = x + iy$
Re z	the real part of z, Re $z = x$
Im z	the imaginary part of z, Im $z = y$
$|z|$	the modulus of z, $|z| = \sqrt{(x^2 + y^2)}$
arg z	the argument of z, arg $z = \arctan \dfrac{y}{x}$
z^*	the complex conjugate of z, $x - iy$
M	a matrix **M**
$\mathbf{M}^{-1}$	the inverse of the matrix **M**
$\mathbf{M}^T$	the transpose of the matrix **M**
det **M**, $|\mathbf{M}|$	the determinant of the square matrix **M**
a	the vector **a**
$\overrightarrow{AB}$	the vector represented in magnitude and direction by the directed line segment AB
â	a unit vector in the direction of **a**
i, j, k	unit vectors in the directions of the cartesian coordinate axes
$|\mathbf{a}|$, a	the magnitude of **a**
$|\overrightarrow{AB}|$, AB	the magnitude of $\overrightarrow{AB}$
a . b	the scalar product of **a** and **b**
a $\times$ **b**	the vector product of **a** and **b**

A, B, C, etc.	events
$A \cup B$	union of the events A and B
$A \cap B$	intersection of the events A and B
$\mathrm{P}(A)$	probability of the event A
A'	complement of the event A
$\mathrm{P}(A\|B)$	probability of the event A conditional on the event B
X, Y, R, etc.	random variables
x, y, r, etc.	values of the random variables X, Y, R, etc.
$x_1, x_2, \ldots$	observations
$f_1, f_2, \ldots$	frequencies with which the observations $x_1, x_2, \ldots$ occur
$\mathrm{p}(x)$	probability function $\mathrm{P}(X = x)$ of the discrete random variable X
$p_1, p_2, \ldots$	probabilities of the values $x_1, x_2, \ldots$ of the discrete random variable X
$\mathrm{f}(x), \mathrm{g}(x), \ldots$	the value of the probability density function of a continuous random variable X
$\mathrm{F}(x), \mathrm{G}(x), \ldots$	the value of the (cumulative) distribution function $\mathrm{P}(X \leqslant x)$ of a continuous random variable X
$\mathrm{E}(X)$	expectation of the random variable X
$\mathrm{E}[\mathrm{g}(X)]$	expectation of $\mathrm{g}(X)$
$\mathrm{Var}(X)$	variance of the random variable X
$\mathrm{G}(t)$	probability generating function for a random variable which takes the values 0, 1, 2, $\ldots$
$\mathrm{B}(n, p)$	binomial distribution with parameters n and p
$\mathrm{N}(\mu, \sigma^2)$	normal distribution with mean μ and variance σ^2
μ	population mean
σ^2	population variance
σ	population standard deviation
$\bar{x}, m$	sample mean
$s^2, \hat{\sigma}^2$	unbiased estimate of population variance from a sample, $$s^2 = \frac{1}{n-1}\sum(x_i - \bar{x})^2$$
ϕ	probability density function of the standardised normal variable with distribution $\mathrm{N}(0, 1)$
Φ	corresponding cumulative distribution function
ρ	product moment correlation coefficient for a population
r	product moment correlation coefficient for a sample
$\mathrm{Cov}\,(X, Y)$	covariance of X and Y

Index

Revise for Heinemann Modular Mathematics for Edexcel AS and A Level

Revision made simple

Heinemann has taken the pain out of revision, with a comprehensive series of easy-to-use revision guides for **Edexcel's Modular Mathematics AS and A Level**. Each book, written by the same team that produces the core books, is designed to tackle each module alongside the core text. The guides are perfect for additional support and guidance throughout the course, or can be used specifically for revision. In each book there are worked examples from real examination papers, comprehensive 'test yourself' sections to check your progress, and all the answers at the back. And if you're finding a particular topic difficult, the revision books refer you back to the core texts, complete with page references, to help you brush up on problem areas.

To see any of the following titles FREE for 60 days or to order your books straight away call Customer Services on 01865 888068

Revise for Pure Mathematics 1
0435 511106

Revise for Pure Mathematics 2
0435 511114

Revise for Pure Mathematics 3
0435 511122

Revise for Mechanics 1
0435 511130

Revise for Mechanics 2
0435 511149

Revise for Mechanics 3
0435 511157

Revise for Statistics 1
0435 511165

Revise for Statistics 2
0435 511173

Revise for Statistics 3
0435 511181

Revise for Decision Mathematics 1
0435 51119X